W9-BMV-738

WORDLY WISE 3000®
BOOK 4
THIRD EDITION

Systematic Academic Vocabulary Development

Kenneth Hodkinson | Sandra Adams

School Specialty, Inc.
Cambridge and Toronto

Editorial Project Manager: Kate Moltz
Senior Editor: Will Tripp
Editor: Rachel Smith
Senior Designer: Deborah Rodman
Cover Design: Michelle Mohnkern

Illustration Credits:
Lessons 1, 4, 6, 10, 12, 13, 16, 17, 19: Q2AMedia.

Photograph Credits: Lesson 2: Fotolia; Lesson 3: Eric Gevaert/Fotolia; Lesson 5: George E. Hansen/ Library of Congress Prints and Photographs Division; Lesson 7: PlanctonVideo/Fotolia; Lesson 8: iStockphoto/Thinkstock; Lesson 9: Clearviewstock/Fotolia; Lesson 11: Fderib/Fotolia; Lesson 14: Olena Turovtseva; Lesson 15: Fotolia; Lesson 18: Masterfile; Lesson 20: Library of Congress Prints and Photographs Division Washington, D.C. 20540 USA.

Printed in Benton Harbor, MI, in December 2011
ISBN 978-0-8388-7604-6

1 2 3 4 5 PPG 15 14 13 12 11

Contents

Welcome to *Wordly Wise 3000*®

You've been learning words since you were a tiny baby. At first, you learned them only by hearing other people talk. Now that you are a reader, you have another way to learn words.

Obviously, it's important to know what words mean, but lots of times, we think we can get away without knowing some of them as we read. This could cause a problem. Say you are reading the directions for a new game. You know most of the words in the sentence you're reading. Then you stop for a word you don't recognize:

> *Please do not touch the* blegmy *or your score will be lost.*

You ask yourself, "What is a *blegmy?*" At first you think, "Well, it's only one word." But then you think, "What is it that I'm not supposed to touch?" All of a sudden, knowing what that one word means is important!

Clearly, the more words you know, the better your understanding of everything you read. *Wordly Wise 3000* will help you learn a lot of words, but it can't teach you *all* the words you'll ever need. It can, however, help guide your learning of new words on your own.

How Do You Learn What Words Mean?

There are two main ways you learn what words mean: directly and indirectly.

You have to learn some words *directly*. You may study them for a class, look them up in a dictionary or glossary, or ask someone what they mean. You also learn word meanings *indirectly* by hearing and reading the words. In fact, the more you listen and read, the more words you'll learn. Reading books, magazines, and online can help build your vocabulary.

At school, you learn a lot of words directly. If you're using this book, you are learning words directly. You are reading the words, learning what they mean, and studying them. Then you are practicing them as you do the activities. Finally, you might even use them in your own writing or conversations. There is an old saying: "Use a word three times and it's yours." Three times might not be enough, of course, but the idea is right. The more you practice using a word, the better you understand it.

What Is "School Language"?

School language—or school words—are the words you find in the books you read, from novels to textbooks, and on tests. You read them online as you look up information. Your teacher uses these words to explain an important concept about math or reading. Some have to do with a particular topic, such as the building of the Great Pyramid in Egypt. Others are words for tasks you are being asked to do, such as *summarize*. These words are different from the kinds of words you use when you're hanging out with your friends or talking casually with your family. That's why you often need to study these words directly.

Wordly Wise 3000 is designed to teach you some of the words you need to do well in school and on tests—and later on in your jobs. It will also help you learn how to learn more words. Remember, there is no single thing that will help you understand what you read as much as knowing word meanings will.

How Do You Figure Out Word Meanings?

What should you do when you come to a word and you think you don't know what it means?

Say It
First, say it to yourself. Maybe once you do this, it will sound like a word you *do* know. Sometimes you know a word in your head without knowing what it looks like in print. So if you match up what you know and what you read—you have the word!

Use Context
If this doesn't work, take the next step: look at the context of the word— the other words and sentences around it. Sometimes these can give you a clue to the word's meaning. Here's an example:

> *Mr. Huerta had great respect for his* opponent.

Say that you don't know what *opponent* means. Does Mr. Huerta have respect for his teacher? His mother? Then you read on:

The two players sat across from each other in the warm room. The chessboard was between them. Both looked as if they were concentrating very hard.

Now you see that Mr. Huerta is taking part in a chess game. You know that in a chess game, one person plays another. So his *opponent* must be the person he is playing against. You reread the sentence using that meaning. Yes, that works. In this sentence, *opponent* means "someone you play against, or compete with."

Use Word Parts

If the context doesn't help, look at the parts of the word. Does it have any prefixes you know? How about suffixes? Or roots? These can help you figure out what it means. Look at this sentence:

Shania had the misfortune *to hurt her arm right before the swim meet.*

If you don't know the meaning of *misfortune*, try looking at parts of the word. You might know that *fortune* means "luck." Maybe *mis-* is a prefix. You could look it up, or maybe you remember its meaning from studying prefixes in school. The prefix *mis-* means a few different things, but one of them is "bad." You try it out and reread the sentence using that meaning. It would certainly be bad luck, or a *misfortune,* to hurt your arm before a swim meet.

Look It Up

If saying the word or using context and word parts don't work, you can look it up in a dictionary—either a book or online reference—or a glossary.

Nobody knows the meaning of every word, but good readers know how to use these strategies to figure out words they don't know. Get into the habit of using them as you read, and you may be surprised at how automatic it becomes!

How Well Do You Know a Word?

It's important to know many words and to keep on learning more. But it's also important to know them well. In fact, some experts say that there are four levels of knowing a word:

1. I never saw/heard it before.
2. I've heard/seen it, but I don't know what it means.
3. I think it has something to do with…
4. I know it.*

Just because you can read a word and have memorized its definition, it doesn't mean that you know that word well. You want to know it so well that you know when to use it and when to use another word instead. One way to help deepen your knowledge of a word is to use a graphic organizer like the one below that tells about the word *portion*.

Concept of Definition Map

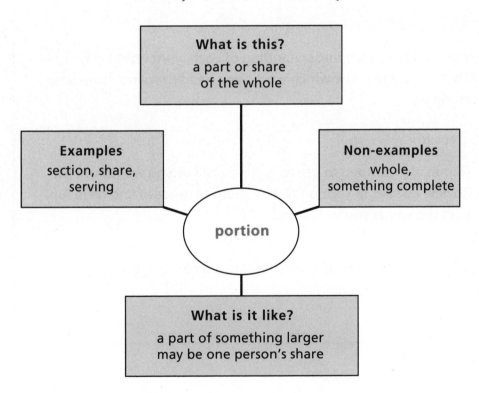

What is this?
a part or share
of the whole

Examples
section, share,
serving

Non-examples
whole,
something complete

portion

What is it like?
a part of something larger
may be one person's share

If you can fill in all the parts of this graphic organizer, you are well on your way to really knowing the word *portion*.

*Dale, E., & O'Rourke, J. (1986). *Vocabulary Building*. Columbus, OH: Zaner-Bloser.

Free Website: WordlyWise3000.com

Did you know you can access *Wordly Wise 3000* online?

Go to www.WordlyWise3000.com and you will find:

Word Lists for all the lessons

The Word Lists allow you to read the words and their definitions and listen to how they are pronounced.

The Word Lists can also be downloaded onto your MP3 player. You can download them and study them wherever you are— home, on the bus, in study period—a great use of your time.

A Quick Check question for every word

You can check your understanding of each word right away. That helps you know which words you need to spend more time studying.

Games for every book

Games are grouped to use as reviews, just as you would use the Review Puzzles in your book. Use them to practice and have fun with the words you've learned.

Good luck in your study of words. It takes some work, but it will pay off in the end.

For more practice and games, go to www.WordlyWise3000.com.

| **Word List** | Study the definitions of the words. Then do the exercises that follow. |

benefit
be´ nə fit

v. To help or be helpful to; to be useful to.
That preschool program **benefits** young children.

n. 1. Something that is useful or helpful, that does good.
One of the **benefits** of my exercise program is that I sleep better.

2. An event held to raise money for a cause.
The library's **benefit** raised enough money for a new children's room.

complete
kəm plēt´

adj. 1. Having no missing parts; whole.
She bought a **complete** set of woodworking tools at a yard sale.

2. Finished.
The new wing on the high school is now **complete**.

v. To finish.
Schubert did not **complete** his eighth symphony, so it's nicknamed "The Unfinished."

develop
di vel´ əp

v. 1. To go through a process of growth.
Running regularly **develops** strong leg muscles.

2. To bring or come into being.
The day after I brushed against the poison ivy, a rash **developed** on my leg.

3. To apply chemicals to photographic film to bring out the picture.
I want to learn to **develop** my own pictures.

dismay
dis mā´

v. To cause feelings of fear, worry, or surprise.
A large crack in the ceiling of our newly painted kitchen **dismayed** my parents.

n. A sudden loss of courage because of fear or worry.
Just after we began hiking, we were filled with **dismay** when we heard the rumble of a rockslide.

ease
ēz

n. A state of being comfortable—without worry, pain, or trouble.
Since I took a course in public speaking, I feel much more at **ease** when I give a speech.

v. To make less worried, pained, or troubled.
It **eased** my mind to hear you were safe.

hail hāl	*n.* Small lumps of frozen rain. The **hail** bouncing off the metal roof of the garage made a terrible racket. *v.* 1. To fall as frozen rain. My father's corn plants suffered a lot of damage when it **hailed** yesterday. 2. To greet or welcome, usually with admiration. The band played "**Hail** to the Chief" as the president came in.
lack lak	*v.* To be without. He never sees the funny side of things because he **lacks** a sense of humor. *n.* A shortage. A **lack** of money to pay the staff forced our library to close on weekends.
master mas´tər	*adj.* 1. Chief; main. Throw the **master** switch to turn on the power. 2. Having or showing great skill. Rick is a **master** carpenter. *v.* To become skilled at. My mother **mastered** the new computer program in just a few weeks.
patriot pā´trē ət	*n.* One who loves, supports, and is loyal to his or her country. Giuseppe Garibaldi was an Italian **patriot** who fought tirelessly to unite his country. **patriotic** (pā trē ä tik) *adj.* Having or showing love of one's country. "America the Beautiful" is a **patriotic** song that was written by Katherine Lee Bates. **patriotism** *n.* Love of one's country. Some people show their **patriotism** by proudly flying their country's flag.
project prä´jekt	*n.* A plan or idea for doing something. My science **project** is going to show what acid rain does to plants. *v.* (prə jekt´) 1. To stick out. Nails are still **projecting** out of the new floor, so be careful where you walk. 2. To cause an image to be shown on a screen. This machine **projects** color slides but not movies.
recommend rə kə mend´	*v.* 1. To make a statement of praise. I loved *The Secret Garden* and I highly **recommend** it. 2. To give advice; to suggest. Dentists usually **recommend** that you have a checkup twice a year.

remark ri märk	*v.* To say; to make a comment. My grandmother **remarked** on how well I looked. *n.* Something said; a comment. When no one else could think of anything to say, I made a **remark** about how badly we needed rain. **remarkable** *adj.* Deserving of being noticed; unusual. For such a young child, he had **remarkable** strength.
represent re pri zent´	*v.* 1. To stand for or in place of. Three dots **represent** the letter "S" in the Morse code. 2. To act in place of. Each state in the U.S. elects two senators to **represent** it in Congress.
sufficient sə fish´ənt	*adj.* Enough to fill a need. Ten lessons on the oboe were **sufficient** to earn me a place in the school band.
utter u´ tər	*v.* To make sounds with the voice; to speak. Please don't **utter** another word.

1A ▷ Finding Meanings

Choose two phrases to form a sentence that correctly uses a word from Word List 1. Write each sentence in the space provided.

1. (a) a useful aid.　　　(c) Dismay is
   (b) Hail is　　　　　　(d) frozen rain.

   _____

   _____

2. (a) A remarkable plan is　　(c) one that will probably fail.
   (b) the main one.　　　　　(d) A master plan is

   _____

   _____

3. (a) a place to relax.　　　　　　(c) A benefit is
   (b) an event that raises money.　(d) A patriot is

   _____

   _____

4. (a) A complete picture is one　　(c) very unusual.
       that is
   (b) A remarkable picture is one　(d) not easy to see.
       that is

   _____

   _____

5. (a) to bring it to an end.　　　(c) to make it grow.
   (b) To develop something is　　(d) To ease something is

   _____

   _____

6. (a) to control it.　　　　　　　(c) To utter something is
   (b) To complete something is　 (d) to say it.

   _____

   _____

7. (a) stand in for him or her.　 (c) To represent someone is to
   (b) invite him or her.　　　　　(d) To recommend someone is to

   _____

   _____

8. (a) To lack food　　　　　　　　(c) is to have more than enough.
   (b) To have sufficient food　 (d) is to have enough.

   _____

   _____

9. (a) to show it on a screen.　　(c) To recommend a picture is
   (b) to change it slightly.　　 (d) To project a picture is

   _____

   _____

benefit

complete

develop

dismay

ease

hail

lack

master

patriot

project

recommend

remark

represent

sufficient

utter

Improve each of the following sentences by crossing out the bold phrase and replacing it with a word (or a form of the word) from Word List 1.

1. I sensed a **total absence** of enthusiasm when I suggested that we climb Mount Monadnock.

2. Martha Graham **brought into being** a new style of dance in America.

3. The bookshelf **sticks out** too far into the room and has to be made narrower.

4. I took a hot bath to help to **take away the pain in** my aching muscles.

5. Olga Ramirez expects her novel to be **at a point where no further work is necessary** by the end of the week.

6. My uncle **became very skilled at speaking** French after spending a year in France.

7. In English, the letter "c" **stands for** two different sounds.

8. Young children **are helped** a great deal from being read to every day.

9. The article ended with a reminder that there is more to showing **love of one's country** than flying your country's flag.

10. The news that the last train had just left **worried and distressed** us.

11. The track coach **gave me the suggestion** that I warm up before starting my run.

Circle the letter or letters of each correct answer. A question may have more than one correct answer.

1. Which of the following might fill someone with **dismay?**
   - (a) losing ten dollars
   - (b) finding ten dollars
   - (c) finding a staple in a tuna sandwich
   - (d) finding celery in a tuna sandwich

2. Which of the following might put someone at **ease?**
   - (a) a friendly smile
   - (b) a "Keep Out" sign
   - (c) a warm welcome
   - (d) a promise to help

3. Which of the following might be **hailed** by people?
   - (a) a train crash
   - (b) a cure for a disease
   - (c) a popular president
   - (d) rain after a long dry spell

4. Which of the following is a **complete** sentence and needs a period?
   - (a) I'm cold
   - (b) Let's go
   - (c) The bus for Toledo
   - (d) My hockey puck

5. A rich person could **lack** which of the following?
   - (a) money
   - (b) freedom
   - (c) time
   - (d) good health

6. Which of the following could mean a person is **patriotic?**
   - (a) making money
   - (b) having a hobby
   - (c) voting in elections
   - (d) serving one's country

7. Which of the following is a **remark?**
   - (a) You look tired.
   - (b) 2 + 2 = 4
   - (c) What on earth are you doing?
   - (d) A B C D

8. Which of the following **represent** other people?
   - (a) state senators
   - (b) taxi drivers
   - (c) storekeepers
   - (d) lawyers

benefit
complete
develop
dismay
ease
hail
lack
master
patriot
project
recommend
remark
represent
sufficient
utter

Synonyms are words that have the same or similar meanings. *Big* and *large* are synonyms. Both words have to do with great size.

Circle the two synonyms in each group of four words.

1. harm   hail   benefit   help

2. rush   finish   complete   lack

3. dismay   develop   grow   need

4. alarm   joy   hunger   dismay

5. ease   growth   comfort   project

6. remark   hail   forget   greet

7. shortage   lack   promise   return

8. suggest   satisfy   recommend   promise

9. comment   remark   disturbance   pause

10. repeat   utter   represent   say

Read the passage. Then answer the questions that follow it.

Sequoya's Gift

Sequoya was a **remarkable** man in many ways. He was a skilled silversmith and painter. He also served as a soldier. But he is remembered today for inventing a written language.

Sequoya was a member of the Cherokee nation, the son of a Native American mother and a British father. A **patriotic** person, he was **dismayed** that white people were taking over more and more of the Cherokee lands.

There was no easy way for Cherokees to be in touch with each other because they **lacked** a written language. Words spoken in Cherokee were lost as soon as they were **uttered.** Sequoya believed that the Cherokee people would **benefit** greatly if they had a written language and could read and write. Newspapers could spread the word of what was happening to people. Books could record their history. He made up his mind that he would try to **develop** a written language for his people.

The **project,** which he began in 1809, took twelve years to **complete.** He and his daughter worked together. She carefully sounded out each syllable. Then Sequoya **represented** each one with a letter that he chose from the English, Greek, and Hebrew alphabets. Eighty-six letters were **sufficient** to cover all the sounds of the Cherokee language.

Sequoya used this new written language in a message he sent to the leaders of the Cherokee nation. The leaders were impressed with how simple the system was. They **recommended** that the new written language be taught to everyone who wanted to learn to read and write. People liked it because it could be learned quickly and with **ease.** Those who **mastered** it went on to teach others. The Cherokees set up schools to teach Sequoya's alphabet and began to publish books and newspapers in their new language. The first Native American newspaper, the *Cherokee Phoenix,* was published on February 21, 1828. It was followed by a flood of other newspapers and books.

In his later years, Sequoya travelled throughout North America studying other Native American languages. Everywhere he went he was **hailed** for his invention, which played such an important part in uniting the Cherokee people. He died in 1843. His memory is honored in California's giant sequoia trees, and its beautiful Sequoia National Park.

benefit
complete
develop
dismay
ease
hail
lack
master
patriot
project
recommend
remark
represent
sufficient
utter

▶ **Answer each of the following questions in the form of a sentence. If a question does not contain a vocabulary word from the lesson's word list, use one in your answer. Use each word only once.**

1. How can we tell that Sequoya was **patriotic?**

_____

_____

2. What is the meaning of **utter** as used in the passage?

_____

_____

3. Why weren't any books written in Cherokee before 1821?

_____

_____

4. How did Sequoya feel about what the white settlers were doing?

_____

_____

5. What is the meaning of **develop** as it is used in the passage?

_____

_____

6. How did Sequoya use the English, Greek, and Hebrew alphabets?

_____

_____

7. Why weren't 26 letters **sufficient** for the Cherokee alphabet?

_____

_____

8. How long did Sequoya's work take?

_____

_____

9. Did Sequoya work on his **project** alone or did he have help?

_____

_____

10. Why was the new language popular with the people?

_____

_____

11. How can we tell that the Cherokee leaders liked the new system?

_____

_____

12. What is the meaning of **hailed** as it is used in the passage?

_____

_____

13. How did the Cherokees help each other learn the new language?

_____

_____

14. What was **remarkable** about Sequoya?

_____

_____

15. How does a written language **benefit** friends living far apart?

_____

_____

benefit
complete
develop
dismay
ease
hail
lack
master
patriot
project
recommend
remark
represent
sufficient
utter

FUN & FASCINATING FACTS

- The Latin bene means "good" and forms a root of the word **benefit.** A benefit is something that is good for a person. Other words formed from this root include benevolent, which means "having a wish to do good," and beneficial, which means "doing good."

- In addition to its meaning as a verb, **utter** is also an adjective and means "total" or "absolute." (When the cellar door slammed shut behind us, we were left in utter darkness.); (I felt like an utter fool when the bike I reported stolen was found just where I left it.)

For more practice and games, go to **www.WordlyWise3000.com**.

Word List

Study the definitions of the words. Then do the exercises that follow.

affect
ə fekt´

v. 1. To bring about a change in.
Do you think changing schools will **affect** my grades?

2. To pretend to be or to have.
The reporter **affected** an interest in buying a used car in order to get the salesperson to talk to her.

calculate
kal´kyōō lāt

v. 1. To find the answer by using arithmetic.
I gave my sister the check so she could **calculate** her share of the bill.

2. To figure out by reasoning.
You'd better **calculate** the risks carefully before going on a long trip with that old car.

climate
klī´ mət

n. The average weather conditions of an area.
Florida's warm **climate** is perfect for growing oranges.

column
kä´ ləm

n. 1. A row of figures or words running down a printed page; anything arranged like that.
Do all the problems in the first **column** on page 30.

2. A tall, usually stone support that holds up something.
Forty-six marble **columns** support the roof of the Parthenon in Athens.

3. A regular newspaper or magazine article usually written by the same person.
My mother writes a weekly sports **column** for the *News-Tribune*.

decay
dē kā´

v. To rot.
Leaves left on the ground will **decay** over the winter.

n. A breaking down or rotting.
Dentists say tooth **decay** can be prevented by regular brushing and flossing.

exceed
ek sēd´

v. 1. To be more than.
The final score of Monday's game **exceeded** our best hopes.

2. To go beyond what is allowed.
The officer who stopped me told me never to **exceed** the speed limit again.

excess (ek ses´) *n.* More than enough; an extra amount.
Use what you need, and save the **excess.**

excessive *adj.* Too much or too great.
Last winter my parents paid an **excessive** amount for heating oil.

forbid
fər bid´

v. To order not to do something.
A state law **forbids** smoking in hospitals.

forbidden *adj.* Not allowed.
Eating in class is **forbidden.**

grove
grōv

n. A group of trees growing together with open space between them.
The children walked hand in hand through the **grove** of lemon trees.

limb
lim

n. 1. An arm, leg, or wing.
Bats use their webbed front and back **limbs** to fly.

2. A large tree branch.
The owl was perched on the top **limb** of the tree.

mammoth
ma´ məth

adj. Very large; huge.
The **mammoth** Seattle Skydome holds over fifty thousand people.

mature
me chŏŏr´

v. To become fully grown or developed.
Rabbits **mature** in about six months and are then able to bear young.

adj. Fully grown or developed; adult.
My brother looks very **mature** for only eleven.

permit
pər mit´

v. To allow.
Some towns **permit** overnight parking downtown.

n. (pʉr´ mit) A written notice that allows a person to do something.
You need a **permit** to go fishing in that lake.

resist
ri zist´

v. 1. To refuse to give in to; to withstand.
Some kinds of corn **resist** disease better than others.

2. To work or fight against.
The armies of Genghis Khan were so powerful, it was useless to **resist** them.

scorch	*v.* To burn slightly.
skôrch	If you press a shirt with an iron that is too hot, you might **scorch** the cloth.
	scorching *adj.* Very hot.
	On such a **scorching** July day, the only thing I wanted after work was a swim in the ocean.

tower	*v.* To stand above or higher than what is around it.
tou´ ər	The Statue of Liberty **towers** above New York Harbor.
	towering *adj.* Very high; tall.
	Looking up at the **towering** skyscrapers gave me a stiff neck.

2A ▶ Finding Meanings

Choose two phrases to form a sentence that correctly uses a word from Word List 2. Write each sentence in the space provided.

1. (a) keep people out of a building.　(c) A column is used to
   (b) support part of a building.　　(d) A permit is used to

   _____

   _____

2. (a) A maple grove is　　　　　　(c) A maple limb is
   (b) what is left after it is cut down.　(d) a large branch.

   _____

3. (a) A mammoth parade is　　　　(c) one held once a year.
   (b) A forbidden parade is　　　　(d) one that is very large.

   _____

4. (a) To scorch something is to　　(c) look closely into it.
   (b) To permit something is to　　(d) allow it.

   _____

   _____

5. (a) A climate is 　　　　　　　　(c) a group of paintings.
　　(b) a group of trees. 　　　　　(d) A grove is

_____

_____

6. (a) To calculate something is to 　(c) To affect something is to
　　(b) figure it out by reasoning. 　(d) be against it.

_____

_____

7. (a) If something towers, 　　　　(c) it is starting to grow.
　　(b) If something decays, 　　　(d) it stands above what is around it.

_____

_____

8. (a) to go beyond it. 　　　　　　(c) To exceed something is
　　(b) To forbid something is 　　(d) to go back to it.

_____

_____

9. (a) To resist something is 　　　(c) to cause a change in it.
　　(b) To affect something is 　　(d) to forget about it.

_____

_____

10. (a) an extra amount. 　　　　　(c) a shortage.
　　(b) A climate is 　　　　　　(d) An excess is

_____

_____

affect
calculate
climate
column
decay
exceed
forbid
grove
limb
mammoth
mature
permit
resist
scorch
tower

Improve each of the following sentences by crossing out the bold phrase and replacing it with a word (or a form of the word) from Word List 2.

1. Pat's **regular newspaper article** on gardening is very popular with readers.

2. Unfortunately, the cost of those sneakers **is more than** what I've saved so far.

3. I tried to **figure out** how much gas we would use on our trip to Nevada.

4. She **pretended to have** a Southern accent, even though she was from New England.

5. Young people **develop into adults** much earlier than they used to.

6. Arizona's **usual weather** is very dry.

7. My parents **do not allow** television during the week.

8. Even though I'm dieting, I find it hard to **avoid giving in to my wish for** fried foods.

9. If you apply heat to a compost pile, it speeds up the **process of the breaking down** of vegetable matter.

10. It is so **extremely hot** today that the plants on our front steps are all drooping.

Circle the letter or letters of each correct answer. A question may have more than one correct answer.

1. Which of the following could be thought of as **towering?**
   (a) an eight-foot person
   (b) an eight-foot tree
   (c) a 100-foot flagpole
   (d) a 100-meter race

2. For which of the following might you need a **permit?**
   (a) camping in a park
   (b) setting lobster traps
   (c) keeping a dog
   (d) owning a goldfish

3. Which of the following help(s) the body to **resist** disease?
   (a) greasy food
   (b) exercise
   (c) germs
   (d) clothing

4. Which of the following **decay(s)?**
   (a) snow and ice
   (b) metal posts
   (c) fallen trees
   (d) cut grass

5. Which of the following are **forbidden?**
   (a) stealing
   (b) cheating
   (c) breathing
   (d) speeding

6. Which of the following can be **scorched?**
   (a) the bark of a tree
   (b) a new shirt
   (c) a clever idea
   (d) a pool of water

7. In which of the following might you see a **grove** of trees?
   (a) a large park
   (b) a large field
   (c) a parking lot
   (d) a tall building

8. Which of the following is a **limb?**
   (a) a bird's wing
   (b) a bird's leg
   (c) a tree branch
   (d) a tree root

affect
calculate
climate
column
decay
exceed
forbid
grove
limb
mammoth
mature
permit
resist
scorch
tower

Antonyms are words that have opposite or nearly opposite meanings. *Enter* and *exit* are antonyms. *Enter* means "to go in," and *exit* means "to go out."

Circle the two antonyms in each group of four words.

1. develop	deny	decay	design
2. exceed	permit	affect	forbid
3. speed	difficulty	ease	care
4. resist	remark	surrender	surprise
5. hurry	start	rush	complete
6. harm	benefit	understand	forget
7. mammoth	tiny	sufficient	mature
8. ease	joy	dislike	dismay
9. angry	childish	mature	unusual
10. lack	prize	award	excess

Read the passage. Then answer the questions that follow it.

California's Forest Giants

Along the coast of northern California grow huge, **towering** trees. Their trunks look like the **columns** of a great Greek temple. These are redwood trees—the tallest of all trees. They can reach a height of 385 feet. Their trunks can grow straight up for 150 feet before the first **limbs** branch out. One redwood, called the Rockefeller Tree, is as tall as a thirty-five-story skyscraper!

Because redwoods are so special, there are laws to protect them. In California, state laws **forbid** people to cut them down in some areas. But in other parts of the state, logging of redwoods is **permitted.** Redwood is sold for use in buildings and outdoor furniture. It is useful because it does not **decay** as quickly as other kinds of wood.

Another enormous California tree is the sequoia. Sequoias are slightly shorter than redwoods. They prefer the colder, drier **climate** found farther inland on the slopes of the Sierra Nevada. Sequoias have thicker trunks and contain more wood than redwoods. In fact, it has been **calculated** that a full-grown sequoia contains enough wood to build thirty houses. The **mammoth** General Grant sequoia is almost a hundred feet around. It would take twenty people with arms stretched out to join hands around it! Cutting down any sequoia is not allowed.

Redwoods and sequoias are among the oldest living things: the age of some of them **exceeds** three thousand years. One reason they live so long has to do with their bark. When they are **mature,** their bark is more than a foot thick. Forest fires don't usually **affect** these trees seriously; the flames only **scorch** their surface. The thick bark also helps them **resist** diseases that kill other trees.

Yosemite National Park and Sequoia National Park are the best places to see sequoias. Both parks are in eastern California. The best place to see redwoods is Redwood National Park, in northwest California. To wander through a **grove** of sequoia or redwood trees is to enter a strange and beautiful world. You will feel like you are walking among giants.

affect
calculate
climate
column
decay
exceed
forbid
grove
limb
mammoth
mature
permit
resist
scorch
tower

▶ **Answer each of the following questions in the form of a sentence. If a question does not contain a vocabulary word from the lesson's word list, use one in your answer. Use each word only once.**

1. What happens to sequoias and redwoods in a forest fire?

_____

_____

2. Where can you find **groves** of redwoods?

_____

_____

3. Are people allowed to cut down redwood tress in all parts of California?

_____

_____

4. How far from the ground are the lowest branches of the redwoods?

_____

_____

5. What do the trunks of redwoods look like?

_____

_____

6. How old are the oldest sequoia and redwood trees?

_____

_____

7. Why is **towering** a good word to use to describe these trees?

_____

_____

8. When is their bark thickest?

_____

_____

9. How does their thick bark help the trees stay healthy?

_____

_____

10. Could you cut down a sequoia?

_____

_____

11. Why is redwood used for building outdoor furniture?

_____

_____

12. Why don't sequoias grow along the coast?

_____

_____

13. How thick is the trunk of the General Grant tree?

_____

_____

14. How much wood does a full-grown sequoia contain?

_____

_____

15. Why have redwoods and sequoias lived so long?

_____

_____

affect
calculate
climate
column
decay
exceed
forbid
grove
limb
mammoth
mature
permit
resist
scorch
tower

FUN & FASCINATING FACTS

- An easy way to learn simple arithmetic is to set out pebbles in a row. By adding more pebbles and counting the total, or by taking some away and counting the ones that remain, one can see the results of addition and subtraction. By using rows of pebbles, one can also learn multiplication. Pebbles arranged in three rows of four can be counted one at a time to see that 3 times 4 equals 12. By separating the pebbles into equal-sized groups, one can also learn division. For example, dividing the pebbles into two equal groups and counting the pebbles in one of them shows that 12 divided by 2 equals six. The Romans long ago thought of this method of doing math. In fact, our word **calculate** comes from the Latin word *calculus,* which means—a pebble!

- Tens of thousands of years ago, a giant elephant lived in Europe and North America. It was called a mammoth. It was bigger than today's elephants; the largest ones were almost fourteen feet from the ground to the shoulder. It had huge tusks that curved downward and a thick, hairy coat. Mammoths died out long ago, but the bodies of some of them were frozen solid in the northern regions of Canada and Russia. They are sometimes found when the ice around them melts. Because of this creature's great size, its name became the adjective **mammoth,** meaning "very large; huge."

For more practice and games, go to **www.WordlyWise3000.com**.

Word List

Study the definitions of the words. Then do the exercises that follow.

approach
ə prōch´

v. To go closer to.
The vet **approached** the wounded deer carefully.

n. 1. A coming closer.
My grandparents dread the **approach** of winter.

2. A road or way that leads to a place.
The **approach** to the beach was blocked by a fallen tree.

burrow
bʉr´ ō

v. 1. To dig a hole or tunnel into or under something.
Turtles **burrow** into soft sand to lay their eggs.

2. To dig deeply into; to search.
The clerk **burrowed** through the pile of papers on his desk.

n. A hole or tunnel dug by an animal as a home or for protection.
A mole spends most of its time in its **burrow.**

cease
sēs

v. To stop; to come or bring to an end.
After several hours of thunder and lightning, the storm finally **ceased.**

destructive
di struk´ tiv

adj. Causing harm or damage.
Cutworms are very **destructive** garden insects.

destruction *n.* Harm or damage.
When Hurricane Katrina hit the Louisiana coast, it caused great **destruction.**

drowsy
drou´ zē

adj. Tired or sleepy.
Lying in the sun always makes my cat, Inky, **drowsy.**

famished
fa´ misht

adj. Very hungry.
Sometimes I work through my lunch hour, so by suppertime I am **famished!**

forecast
fôr´ kast

v. To figure out and say what will happen before it takes place.
Our fishing guide **forecast** a good catch.

n. A telling of what will happen.
As soon as Carlos gets up, he turns on the weather **forecast.**

hibernate
hī bər nāt

v. To spend the winter in a resting state.
Groundhogs **hibernate** because they can't find enough food in the winter.

migrate
mī´ grāt

v. To move from one country or region to another.
Hundreds of thousands of people have **migrated** to the United States in search of freedom.

migration　*n.* The act of migrating.
My friend Sandhya is studying Indian **migration** to the United States.

migratory (mī´ grətôr ē) *adj.* Moving from one place or country to another, usually regularly.
Canada geese are **migratory** birds.

nestle
ne´ səl

v. 1. To settle down comfortably, as if in a nest.
"The children were **nestled** all snug in their beds" is a famous line from *'Twas the Night before Christmas*.

2. To lie in a sheltered, partly hidden place.
The little Swiss town **nestled** at the foot of the Alps.

observe
əb zʉrv´

v. 1. To see; to notice.
I looked up at the sky and **observed** a hawk circling slowly, far above us.

2. To comment; to remark.
Sleepily, I **observed** that it was time we left.

3. To mark an event or day.
We **observed** Martin Luther King Day by closing the store.

4. To obey.
I try to **observe** the speed limit when I drive.

prepare
pri par´

v. To make or get ready.
The scouts **prepared** for their camping trip by getting lots of freeze-dried food.

preparation (pre pə rā´ shən) *n.* Something done to get ready.
Antonio and Ruth did most of the **preparation** for the cookout the night before.

reduce
ri dōōs´

v. To make or become smaller or less.
This winter, Vermont **reduced** the amount of salt it put on its roads.

reduction (ri duk´ shən) *n.* The act of reducing or the amount by which something is reduced.
The store sold out of swimsuits after its huge price **reduction.**

severe
sə vir´

adj. 1. Very strict or harsh.
That's a very **severe** punishment for turning a paper in late.

2. Hard to bear or deal with.
A **severe** frost caused a lot of damage to central Florida's orange crop.

venture	v. To dare to do, to go, or to say.
ven´chər	Maria **ventured** onto the dance floor even though she didn't know how to dance.
	n. Something that involves the risk of a loss.
	Grandpa's most successful **venture** was a carpet cleaning service.

3A ▶ Finding Meanings

Choose two phrases to form a sentence that correctly uses a word from Word List 3. Write each sentence in the space provided.

1. (a) does a lot of damage.   (c) can be easily tamed.
   (b) A migratory animal is one that   (d) A destructive animal is one that

   _____

   _____

2. (a) a disappearance.   (c) An approach is
   (b) A venture is   (d) a coming closer.

   _____

   _____

3. (a) A famished creature   (c) moves with the changing seasons.
   (b) A migratory creature   (d) goes to sleep for the winter.

   _____

   _____

4. (a) To burrow is to   (c) refuse to obey.
   (b) dig a hole or tunnel.   (d) To nestle is to

   _____

   _____

5. (a) to take no part in it.   (c) to say it will happen.
   (b) To forecast an event is   (d) To observe an event is

   _____

   _____

approach
burrow
cease
destructive
drowsy
famished
forecast
hibernate
migrate
nestle
observe
prepare
reduce
severe
venture

6. (a) To reduce is to   (c) To nestle is to
   (b) settle down comfortably.   (d) fall into a deep sleep.

_____

_____

7. (a) Preparation is   (c) Hibernation is
   (b) what you do to get ready.   (d) what is asked for.

_____

_____

8. (a) something that involves a risk.   (c) A reduction is
   (b) the addition of something.   (d) A venture is

_____

_____

9. (a) very thirsty.   (c) To be famished is to be
   (b) very hungry.   (d) To be drowsy is to be

_____

_____

10. (a) To observe something is to   (c) To cease something is to
    (b) pay no attention to it.   (d) notice it.

_____

_____

Improve each of the following sentences by crossing out the bold phrase and replacing it with a word (or a form of the word) from Word List 3.

1. Hana was starting to feel **very sleepy** when a noise made her jump.

2. The rain did not **come to an end** until early the next morning.

3. Some animals **go into a long, deep sleep** because there is so little for them to eat during the winter months.

4. The cottage **lay partly hidden** in a hollow near a grove of poplar trees.

5. All the **roads that lead** to the airport are closed because of the snowstorm.

6. The **long journey** of Canada geese from northern Canada to South America occurs each fall.

7. Even though Granny has **very bad** arthritis, she takes a walk every day.

8. The **cutting down in size** of this week's newspaper to just four pages was due to the paper shortage.

9. Ron **dug deeply** through the papers on his desk, trying to find the letter from his father.

10. As Maria Tipo played the piano, I **closely watched** the way she used the pedal.

approach
burrow
cease
destructive
drowsy
famished
forecast
hibernate
migrate
nestle
observe
prepare
reduce
severe
venture

Circle the letter or letters of each correct answer. A question may have more than one correct answer.

1. Which of the following can people **reduce?**
   - (a) their weight
   - (b) their shoe size
   - (c) their age
   - (d) their spending

2. Which of the following would be a **severe** punishment?
   - (a) a slap on the wrist
   - (b) going to jail
   - (c) no television for a day
   - (d) being told to be quiet

3. Which of the following can a person **forecast?**
   - (a) the final score of a game
   - (b) the weather
   - (c) a past event
   - (d) costs of doing business

4. Which of the following can cause **destruction?**
   - (a) forest fires
   - (b) floods
   - (c) bombs
   - (d) hurricanes

5. Which of the following could **cease?**
   - (a) fighting
   - (b) noises
   - (c) the weather
   - (d) a storm

6. Which of the following can **migrate?**
   - (a) animals
   - (b) birds
   - (c) plants
   - (d) humans

7. Which of the following could be **observed?**
   - (a) a law
   - (b) a birthday
   - (c) a rule
   - (d) a full moon

8. Which of the following can be **prepared?**
   - (a) a lunch for four
   - (b) a garden for planting
   - (c) a book report
   - (d) a full moon

Many English words come from Latin. We say they have Latin roots. Our word *patriot*, for example, is formed from the Latin word *pater*, meaning "father."

In each space, write the Latin word that the English word comes from. Then write its meaning. Choose from the ten Latin words shown.

propius (near)   *plere* (complete)   *bene* (well)
calculus (pebble)   *severus* (serious; strict) *hibernus* (winter)
fames (hunger)   *servare* (watch)   *jacere* (throw)
cessare (stop)

Definition	English Word	Latin Word
1. to draw near; to get closer	approach	_____
Meaning _____		
2. to spend the winter sleeping	hibernate	_____
Meaning _____		
3. very hungry; starving	famished	_____
Meaning _____		
4. to bring to an end; to finish	complete	_____
Meaning _____		
5. to come to an end; to stop	cease	_____
Meaning _____		
6. to look at closely	observe	_____
Meaning _____		
7. strict or harsh	severe	_____
Meaning _____		
8. to throw onto a screen	project	_____
Meaning _____		

approach
burrow
cease
destructive
drowsy
famished
forecast
hibernate
migrate
nestle
observe
prepare
reduce
severe
venture

9. to be useful to; to help   benefit   _____

Meaning _____

10. to figure out using math   calculate   _____

Meaning _____

3E ▷ **Passage**

Read the passage. Then answer the questions that follow it.

A Long Winter Nap

Summer is a good time of year for most animals. It's easy for them to keep warm, and food is plentiful. Winter is harder for them. Lakes and ponds are frozen, and snow may cover the ground. All this makes food much harder to find. Many birds and some animals escape northern winters completely. They **migrate** south in the fall and return in the spring.

The groundhog, or woodchuck, deals with winter differently. It **hibernates.** As soon as it feels the weather turning cold, it starts to dig. It digs a **burrow** at least five feet underground. There it makes a comfortable nest with leaves and grass. The groundhog spends the cold winter months **nestled** in its underground bed. It does not usually wake up until spring. It is far enough below ground that there is no danger of its freezing to death. It stays safe even during the most **severe** winter.

The groundhog does not eat at all during the winter. Instead, it eats as much and as often as it can during the summer. People with gardens know how **destructive** a groundhog can be to their plants. As winter **approaches,** the groundhog becomes so fat it can hardly move. It **prepares** its nest and closes off the openings of the tunnels that lead down to it. When it starts to feel **drowsy,** it makes itself comfortable and falls into a long, deep sleep. This sleep can last up to eight months.

If you **observed** the groundhog in this state, you might think it had died. Its breathing almost **ceases;** its heart slows to about four beats a minute. A thermometer would show that its body temperature has fallen to just above freezing. When the groundhog wakes up in the spring, it has been without food for many months. Its weight has been **reduced** to only half of what it was in the fall. Almost all its body fat has been used up to keep it alive during its long sleep. By February or March, the **famished** animal is ready to leave its hole and go looking for its first meal.

Years ago, people who lived in the country eagerly awaited the sight of the first groundhog putting its head above ground; it was a sign that winter was over. This gave rise to a number of stories. One of them was told by German farmers who had settled in Punxsutawney, Pennsylvania. The story was about a groundhog they called Punxsutawney Phil. This remarkable animal could **forecast** the weather.

According to the story, Phil **ventured** from his nest every February 2. He poked his head above ground and looked around. If he saw his shadow, it meant that there would be another month and a half of winter. In that case, he went back to sleep for another six weeks. If the weather was cloudy, and he didn't see his shadow, it meant spring would be early. This story spread around the country. Eventually, February 2 became known as Groundhog Day.

▶ **Answer each of the following questions in the form of a sentence. If a question does not contain a vocabulary word from the lesson's word list, use one in your answer. Use each word only once.**

1. Why do you almost never see groundhogs in winter?

_____

_____

2. What **preparations** does a groundhog make for winter?

_____

_____

3. How does the groundhog's appearance change as winter **approaches?**

_____

_____

4. How does a groundhog feel just before it begins its long sleep?

_____

_____

approach
burrow
cease
destructive
drowsy
famished
forecast
hibernate
migrate
nestle
observe
prepare
reduce
severe
venture

5. How do groundhogs keep from freezing during the winter months?

_____

_____

6. What might the temperature be during a **severe** winter?

_____

_____

7. How do we know that a groundhog needs only a little oxygen during its winter sleep?

_____

_____

8. What does the groundhog do when it gets into its **burrow?**

_____

_____

9. How does the groundhog's size change over the winter?

_____

_____

10. What is the meaning of **observe** as it is used in the passage?

_____

_____

11. Why is the groundhog **famished** when it wakes up in early spring?

_____

_____

12. What was unusual about Punxsutawney Phil?

_____

_____

13. What is supposed to happen on Groundhog Day?

_____

_____

14. What do many northern birds do to escape the winter?

_____

_____

15. Why do gardeners think groundhogs are **destructive?**

_____

_____

FUN & FASCINATING FACTS

- French, Spanish, and Italian are Latin languages. This means that many of their words come directly from the Latin that people throughout the Roman Empire spoke two thousand years ago. For example, you learned the Latin word *hibernum,* meaning winter. The French word for *winter, hiver,* also comes from Latin.

- When modern science began several hundred years ago, there was a need for scientific terms, and these were usually formed from Latin, the language of scholars. The word **hibernate** was formed in this way. It means "to go into a sleeplike state during the winter," and comes from the Latin word for *winter.*

Lesson 4

Study the definitions of the words. Then do the exercises that follow.

active
ak´ tiv

adj. 1. Taking part; working.
Luis has been an **active** member of the chess club for two years.

2. Lively; quick; busy.
Even though she is over ninety, Dr. O'Brien still has a very **active** mind.

3. Moving a lot; moving quickly.
Since I've been more physically **active,** I can run around the track more easily.

astound
ə stound´

v. To surprise; to amaze.
The United States **astounded** the world in 1969 by landing people on the moon.

astounding *adj.* Very surprising.
The report of flying saucers landing on the White House lawn would be **astounding** if it were true.

attend
ə tend´

v. 1. To go to or be present at.
If you are planning to **attend** the lunchroom committee meeting, please let Mr. Minh know.

2. To pay attention to.
The judge asked the jury to **attend** carefully to what she was going to say.

cherish
cher´ ish

v. 1. To cling to an idea or feeling.
Ramona **cherished** the hope that her father would return soon.

2. To take good care of; to love.
I **cherish** the gold watch my grandfather gave me.

contract
kən trakt´

v. 1. To make an agreement that has the force of law.
We **contracted** with carpenters to repair the stairs.

2. To get; to come to have.
When I **contracted** chicken pox, Dr. Robey told me I had to stay away from other people.

3. To make or become smaller.
By 1828, Cherokee lands had **contracted** to one-tenth the size they had been a hundred years earlier.

n. (kän´ trakt) An agreement that has the force of law.
Tom has just signed a **contract** with a publisher for his first book on the copper miners.

eager
ē´ gər

adj. Wanting very much.
We were **eager** to take part in the science project.

eagerly *adv.* With a great deal of enthusiasm, wanting.
We **eagerly** awaited the arrival of our cousins, whom we hadn't seen in several months.

expose
ek spōz´

v. 1. To make known.
In her weekly newspaper column, Molly Ivins **exposed** the plan to cut health benefits.

2. To open to view.
Cleaning the painting **exposed** the original colors.

3. To leave unprotected.
Since I had no place to keep my bike, I had to leave it outside, **exposed** to the weather.

grace
grās

n. 1. Beauty of form or movement.
Margot Fonteyn danced with such **grace** that she was hailed as one of the world's greatest ballerinas.

2. A short prayer said before a meal.
They always say **grace** in her family.

3. An extra period to do or pay something.
The painters had three days' **grace** to finish the house.

graceful *adj.* Having beauty of movement.
With a **graceful** leap, the cat landed on my lap.

impose
im pōz´

v. 1. To force someone to accept or put up with.
The new coach **imposed** strict rules about arriving late or leaving practice early.

2. To take unfair advantage of.
I try not to **impose** on my mother's good nature.

modest
mä´ dəst

adj. 1. Not thinking too highly of oneself.
Nadia was too **modest** to accept all the credit for her part in producing the play.

2. Simple; not fancy or extreme.
The Wallmans lived in the same **modest** apartment all their lives.

modesty *n.* The quality of being modest.
My sense of **modesty** keeps me from taking too much credit for the project's success.

parallel
par´ ə lel

adj. Lying in the same direction and always the same distance apart.
The two edges of a ruler are **parallel.**

paralyze par´ ə līz	*v.* 1. To stop all movement or feeling in. As the huge wave approached, fear **paralyzed** people walking at the water's edge and they stood there motionless. 2. To make helpless or powerless. The snowstorm **paralyzed** Washington, D.C., for five days. **paralysis** (pə ra´ lə səs) *n.* Condition of being paralyzed. President Franklin D. Roosevelt used a wheelchair because of the **paralysis** of his legs.
pessimist pe´ sə mist	*n.* A person who expects things to turn out badly. A **pessimist** carries an umbrella even though the forecast is for fine weather. **pessimistic** *adj.* Not having hope, joy, or confidence; gloomy. After losing her librarian's job, Ms. Merkelson was **pessimistic** about finding another library position in the same town.
recite ri sīt´	*v.* To say aloud before an audience, usually from memory. Rozzie **recited** her favorite Emily Dickinson poem to the class. **recital** *n.* A program of music or dance. I felt very nervous before my ballet **recital.**
respond ri spänd´	*v.* To answer. When you want to **respond** to a question, please raise your hand. **response** *n.* Something said or done in reply. Henry took a few moments to think before giving his **response** to Mr. Bartlett's question.

 4A ▶ Finding Meanings

Choose two phrases to form a sentence that correctly uses a word from Word List 4. Write each sentence in the space provided.

1. (a) to love that person.
   (b) To cherish someone is
   (c) To expose someone is
   (d) to fear that person.

_____

_____

2. (a) A response is   (c) Paralysis is
   (b) an increase in size.   (d) an answer.

   _____

   _____

3. (a) that causes shock and surprise. (c) An eager reply is one
   (b) An astounding reply is one   (d) that is not spoken.

   _____

   _____

4. (a) To contract is   (c) to make an agreement.
   (b) To attend is   (d) to be afraid.

   _____

   _____

5. (a) are not hidden from view.   (c) Parallel beams
   (b) Exposed beams   (d) meet at a corner.

   _____

   _____

6. (a) To attend a speech is   (c) to make changes in it.
   (b) To recite a speech is   (d) to be present at it.

   _____

   _____

7. (a) affects an interest in   (c) A pessimistic person
       something.
   (b) An eager person   (d) is quick to take part in something.

   _____

   _____

8. (a) Graceful lines are   (c) the same distance apart.
   (b) Parallel lines are   (d) curving away from each other.

   _____

   _____

active

astound

attend

cherish

contract

eager

expose

grace

impose

modest

parallel

paralyze

pessimist

recite

respond

9. (a) a loss of the ability to move.   (c) a belief that things will turn out badly.

   (b) Modesty is   (d) Paralysis is

_____

_____

10. (a) A recital is   (c) A pessimist is
    (b) a written agreement.   (d) one who is gloomy.

_____

_____

11. (a) Grace is   (c) beauty of movement.
    (b) Modesty is   (d) failing to do what is right.

_____

_____

4B Just the Right Word

Improve each of the following sentences by crossing out the bold phrase and replacing it with a word (or a form of the word) from Word List 4.

1. Where the paint has peeled off the house, the wood will be **left unprotected** and unable to stand up to scorching summer heat and severe winter cold.

2. The magician promised that his next trick would **create great amazement in** us.

3. Eleanor Roosevelt's **lack of feelings of self-importance** impressed all who knew her.

4. Heavy snow **stopped the movement of** traffic in Denver for two days.

5. The librarian gave me one week's **extra time** to pay the fine.

6. Only about half of the members of the gardening club are **taking part in what is going on.**

7. Unfortunately, my roommate is **always expecting things to turn out badly,** so he's not a very cheerful person to live with.

8. I was afraid I was **forcing myself on them** when I stayed an extra week at the Mendelssohns'.

9. The pupil of the eye **becomes smaller** in bright light.

10. Did you **give your attention** to your homework?

4C Applying Meanings

Circle the letter or letters of each correct answer. A question may have more than one correct answer.

1. Which of the following could a person **attend?**
   (a) a benefit   (c) a meeting
   (b) a concert   (d) a remark

2. Which of the following can be **contracted?**
   (a) an illness   (c) muscles
   (b) the pupils of the eyes (d) a habit

3. Which of the following requires a person to be **active?**
   (a) playing hockey   (c) walking the dog
   (b) washing windows   (d) watching television

4. Which of the following can be **paralyzed?**
   (a) a person's lower limbs (c) a person's hair
   (b) a person's body   (d) a person's clothes

5. Which of the following might a **modest** person say?
   (a) "I had very little to do with it." (c) "You deserve all the credit."
   (b) "Please don't bother to   (d) "I am the greatest!"
       thank me."

active
astound
attend
cherish
contract
eager
expose
grace
impose
modest
parallel
paralyze
pessimist
recite
respond

6. Which of the following might a **pessimistic** person say?
   (a) "Everything will be all right." (c) "We're bound to lose."
   (b) "It's no use trying."   (d) "Next time we'll try harder."

7. Which of the following are **parallel?**
   (a) the opposite sides of a square (c) the letters A, E, and O
   (b) the three sides of a triangle   (d) the numbers 1, 2, and 3

8. Which of the following would you expect to be **graceful?**
   (a) a beginning skier   (c) a Broadway dancer
   (b) an Olympic diver   (d) an Olympic skater

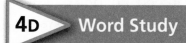

Word Study

Circle the two synonyms in each group of words.

1. astound	amaze	benefit	lack
2. remember	observe	forget	notice
3. mammoth	huge	mature	eager
4. severe	eager	willing	drowsy
5. expose	cherish	love	prepare

Circle the two antonyms in each group of words.

6. pessimistic	remarkable	sufficient	hopeful
7. drowsy	modest	complete	active
8. boastful	destructive	famished	modest
9. recite	expose	impose	hide
10. approach	migrate	enlarge	reduce

Read the passage. Then answer the questions that follow it.

One Step at a Time

Sucheng Chan was an **active** child. She loved to run outside and play with the other children in the village in China where she was born. But in 1943, when she was four years old, she **contracted** a childhood disease called polio. Polio can make people very sick and often causes **paralysis.** The muscles in Sucheng Chan's legs slowly wasted away, and she could no longer run or even walk. The doctors were **pessimistic** about her chances of living more than a year or two. They did not know what a determined person Sucheng Chan was.

For three years, Sucheng Chang lay helplessly in bed. But one day she surprised her mother. Sucheng Chan asked her mother to set up some chairs in two **parallel** lines, their backs facing. She then forced herself out of bed. Slowly, she made her way between the chairs, using their backs as support. She did this time after time. Her body ached from her many falls.

At that time, China was at war with Japan. Sucheng Chan's father was serving in the army, unable to see his family. He **cherished** his daughter, though. It saddened him that he could not give her the comfort and support she needed. When the war ended, he finally returned home. Imagine how **astounded** he was to see Sucheng Chan walk up to him and welcome him! Her movements were jerky and not at all **graceful.** But to her father, there had never been such a beautiful sight.

Sucheng Chan had always been a bright child. She was **eager** to go to school. But in those days in China, education was not free, and her parents had only a **modest** income. Sucheng Chan was eight years old before they had saved enough money for her to **attend** the American school in Shanghai. There she learned to speak English. She also began a lifelong study of Asian history.

In 1948, at the end of Sucheng Chan's first year in school, China's government became communist. The new government **imposed** strict rules forbidding contact with foreigners. One result was that the American school was closed. Sucheng Chan and her parents grew increasingly unhappy. They decided to leave China and settle in Malaysia.

active

astound

attend

cherish

contract

eager

expose

grace

impose

modest

parallel

paralyze

pessimist

recite

respond

Sucheng Chan spent her teenage years at a Malaysian high school. This was the happiest time of her life. She did very well in school and took piano lessons. Sometimes she gave **recitals** for visitors. Once, while walking across the stage, her legs gave way and she fell. She heard a voice say, "Ayah! A baikah (cripple) should not **expose** herself like that." Sucheng Chan's **response** was to struggle to her feet, walk to the piano, and sit down. She played so beautifully that the audience was moved to tears.

After graduating from high school, Sucheng Chan went on to win scholarships to the University of Hawaii. She later became a professor of history and director of Asian American studies at the University of California, Santa Barbara. She led a full and active life. Doctors told her that she might need a wheelchair by the time she was forty; polio's lasting effects can cause more damage to muscles. The doctors were right. But, Sucheng Chan did not let the wheelchair stop her. "I use it only when I am *not* in a hurry," she said.

▶ **Answer each of the following questions in the form of a sentence. If a question does not contain a vocabulary word from the lesson's word list, use one in your answer. Use each word only once.**

1. Why didn't Sucheng Chan go to school until she was eight?

   _____

   _____

2. Why did it become impossible for Sucheng Chan to run outside and play?

   _____

   _____

3. Did her doctors expect Sucheng Chan to get better?

   _____

   _____

4. What usually happens to people who **contract** polio?

   _____

   _____

5. What is the meaning of **active** as it is used in the passage?

_____

_____

6. How does the passage suggest that her father often thought of Sucheng Chan while he was away?

_____

_____

7. Why was Sucheng Chan's father **astounded** when he saw his daughter after the war?

_____

_____

8. Why wasn't Sucheng Chan **graceful?**

_____

_____

9. How did Sucheng Chan feel about going to school?

_____

_____

10. What is the meaning of **attend** as it is used in the passage?

_____

_____

11. Why don't **parallel** lines ever meet?

_____

_____

12. Why do you think China **imposed** rules against contact with foreigners?

_____

_____

13. How can you tell that Sucheng Chan played the piano well?

_____

_____

active

astound

attend

cherish

contract

eager

expose

grace

impose

modest

parallel

paralyze

pessimist

recite

respond

14. What did the person who remarked that Sucheng Chan "should not **expose** herself like that" expect her to do?

_____

_____

15. What might Sucheng Chan's **response** have been if she were not such a determined person?

_____

_____

FUN & FASCINATING FACTS

- Antonyms are words that are opposite in meaning. The antonym of *contract* in its meaning of "to make or become smaller" is *expand*. Metals contract as they get colder; they expand as they get warmer.

- *Pessimist* and *optimist* are another pair of antonyms. An *optimist* has a cheerful outlook on life and expects things to go well. *Pessimist* is formed from the Latin word *pessimus*, which means "worst." *Optimist* is formed from the Latin word *optimus,* which means "best." There is a saying that a pessimist is a person who looks upon the glass as being half-empty; an optimist is a person who looks upon it as being half-full.

Crossword Puzzle Solve the crossword puzzle by studying the clues and filling in the answer boxes. Clues followed by a number are definitions of vocabulary words in lessons 1 through 4. The number gives the lesson from which the answer to the clue is taken.

Clues Across

1. Having no missing parts (1)
5. To rot (2)
8. To be present at (4)
10. To speak (1)
12. The Atlantic _____
13. To make less painful (1)
14. One, _____ , three
16. To make larger or better (1)
18. To make ready (3)
20. A group of trees growing together (2)
23. A stomach _____
26. To burn slightly (2)
29. Lively; quick; busy (4)
30. To cause fear, worry, or surprise (1)
31. To greet or welcome (1)
32. A hole or tunnel dug by an animal (3)
33. Very high (2)
34. Very strict or harsh (3)

Clues Down

2. Fully grown (2)
3. Wanting very much to do or get (4)
4. To dare to do, to go, or to say (3)
6. To go beyond something (2)
7. The _____ is a fort in San Antonio.
9. To draw in an aimless kind of way
11. Something said or expressed (1)
15. To come closer (3)
17. Loss of ability to do or feel (4)
19. Something laid by a bird
21. A paper allowing one to do something (2)
22. One who loves and supports his country(1)
24. An areas' average weather conditions(2)
25. To lie in a sheltered, partly hidden place (3)
27. A row of figures running down a page (2)
28. Red and blue, for example

For more practice and games, go to www.WordlyWise3000.com.

Lesson 5

abrupt
ə brupt´

adj. Happening suddenly, without warning.
When the bus made an **abrupt** stop, several people were thrown off balance.

achieve
ə chēv´

v. To do what one sets out to do.
Even though she was blind and deaf, Helen Keller **achieved** her goal of graduating from college.

achievement *n.* Something done that takes skill or effort.
Landing astronauts on the moon was a great **achievement.**

attempt
ə tempt´

v. To try; to make an effort.
When I **attempted** to leave class early, the teacher asked me to wait until the period was over.

n. A try.
The athlete cleared the bar in the high jump on her third **attempt.**

contempt
kən tempt´

n. A feeling that someone or something is bad or unworthy.
Their classmates felt nothing but **contempt** for those who refused to help the new student.

entertain
en tər tān´

v. 1. To interest and amuse.
My little brother Ramon **entertained** himself for hours with his new paints.

2. To have guests.
We **entertained** some old friends on Thanksgiving weekend.

3. To have in mind.
Lin is **entertaining** the idea of going to soccer camp next summer.

glimpse
glimps

v. To get a quick look at.
I **glimpsed** a black bear near our campground.

n. A quick or hasty look.
I was thrilled to get a **glimpse** of Pavarotti leaving the opera house.

mock
mäk

v. To make fun of.
Cinderella's stepsisters **mocked** her for thinking she could go to the ball.

adj. Not real; pretended.
Mock turtle soup is really made of veal broth, not turtle meat.

persist
pər sist´

v. 1. To keep on doing or trying.
In spite of many falls on the ice, I **persisted** and finally did a figure-eight.

2. To go on and on.
If this rain **persists,** we'll have to cut our vacation short.

persistence *n.* Sticking to something; not giving up.
Emil's **persistence** was rewarded when the tenth law school he applied to accepted him.

persistent *adj.* Refusing to give up.
The **persistent** reporter kept asking questions until she had found out all there was to know about the case.

persuade
pər swād´

v. To win someone over by arguing or asking.
Frank finally **persuaded** me to read *The Adventures of Tom Sawyer*.

persuasive *adj.* Having the power to persuade.
Mary was so **persuasive** that we agreed to help her paint her room.

phase
fāz

n. A stage in a series of changes.
The full moon is one of the **phases** of the moon.

quaint
kwānt

adj. Odd or unusual in a pleasing or old-fashioned way.
Wooden shoes seem **quaint** to Americans, but not to the people of Holland.

recall
ri kôl´

v. 1. To remember.
Do you **recall** what time we left for the soccer game?

2. To call or take back.
The manufacturer **recalled** the cars because of a problem in the steering.

reject
ri jekt´

v. To refuse to accept or use.
The school board **rejected** the plan for the new gym because its cost was excessive.

n. (rē´ jekt) Something that falls short of what is acceptable.
Peter buys factory **rejects** at the pottery store for much less than the price of perfect pieces.

revise
ri vīz´

v. 1. To go over carefully in order to correct or improve.
I don't like to **revise** my stories, but I have to admit they get better when I do.

2. To change in order to bring up to date.
The publishers of that dictionary **revise** it every eight or ten years.

sensitive	*adj.* 1. Quick to notice or feel.
sen´ sə tiv	My doctor is very **sensitive** to my feelings.
	2. Easily affected by even slight change.
	Film used in cameras is very **sensitive** to light.

Choose two phrases to form a sentence that correctly uses a word from Word List 5. Write each sentence in the space provided.

1. (a) one stage in a process.   (c) A glimpse is
   (b) something overheard.   (d) A phase is

   _____

   _____

2. (a) An achievement is   (c) Contempt is
   (b) something done by making   (d) something that is changed.
       an effort.

   _____

   _____

3. (a) loud noise.   (c) A glimpse is a
   (b) quick look.   (d) A reject is a

   _____

   _____

4. (a) Persistence is   (c) a feeling that something is
                                         unworthy.
   (b) Contempt is   (d) a wish to do better.

   _____

   _____

5. (a) that is not accepted.   (c) An attempt is something
   (b) that goes on longer than   (d) A reject is something
       expected.

   _____

   _____

6. (a) Sensitive people

   (b) expect the worst to happen.

   (c) are skilled at getting their ideas across.

   (d) Persuasive people

   _____

   _____

7. (a) To attempt something is to
   (b) try to do it.

   (c) take it back.
   (d) To revise something is to

   _____

   _____

8. (a) give up.
   (b) To persist is to

   (c) refuse to give up.
   (d) To recall is to

   _____

   _____

9. (a) To mock an idea is to
   (b) give it serious thought.

   (c) To entertain an idea is to
   (d) keep it to oneself.

   _____

   _____

10. (a) To recall something is
    (b) To revise something is

    (c) to take it back.
    (d) to throw it with force.

    _____

    _____

abrupt

achieve

attempt

contempt

entertain

glimpse

mock

persist

persuade

phase

quaint

recall

reject

revise

sensitive

Improve each of the following sentences by crossing out the bold phrase and replacing it with a word (or a form of the word) from Lesson 5.

1. This thermometer is very **quick to show changes** to the temperature.

2. His top hat and long cape seemed **pleasingly old-fashioned** to the audience.

3. The **unexpectedly sudden** change in the weather surprised everyone.

4. Juanita **did what she set out to do, which was to get** a perfect score on the test.

5. We **had people staying with us** almost every weekend last summer.

6. If the fog **goes on for a long time,** the plane will be unable to leave on time.

7. The coach **made fun of** the shortstop's unusual way of running.

8. I **caught a quick look at** him through the window of the bus.

9. She needs to **make changes in** her speech before she gives it.

10. Each **stage in the series of changes** must be carefully planned or the project will fail.

Circle the letter or letters of each correct answer. A question may have more than one correct answer.

1. Which of the following can be **sensitive?**
   (a) a person's clothing
   (b) a person's hearing
   (c) a person's feelings
   (d) a person's skin

2. Which of the following might a person think **quaint?**
   (a) a full moon
   (b) an old Valentine card
   (c) a hundred-year-old toy
   (d) pictures in a 1910 book of fairy tales

3. Which of the following might a person **glimpse?**
   (a) someone leaving a crowded room
   (b) a letter someone is trying to hide
   (c) a loud noise
   (d) a strange smell

4. Which of the following can a person **achieve?**
   (a) a goal one sets for oneself
   (b) a calm frame of mind
   (c) naturally curly hair
   (d) high marks on a test

5. Which of the following would you probably **reject?**
   (a) a chance to attend college
   (b) an offer of a ride from a stranger
   (c) bad advice
   (d) an unworkable plan

6. Which of the following might be **persistent?**
   (a) a flash of lightning
   (b) cold and rainy weather
   (c) a back pain
   (d) a bad smell

7. Which of the following can be **revised?**
   (a) a written report
   (b) a person's height
   (c) a set of calculations
   (d) a weather forecast

8. Which of the following might be **entertaining?**
   (a) a magician's tricks
   (b) a football game
   (c) a bus timetable
   (d) an aching tooth

abrupt
achieve
attempt
contempt
entertain
glimpse
mock
persist
persuade
phase
quaint
recall
reject
revise
sensitive

Some things have just one part, and some things have more than one part. A brick has just one part. So does a baseball bat. A box has a bottom, four sides, and a top. Your body is made up of a head, a trunk, and four limbs.

Some words, too, have just one part, and some words have more than one part. There are names for these different parts. The main part of a word is called its *root*. You will remember roots from Lesson 3. Our word *patriotic* is formed from the Latin root *pater,* meaning "father."

A prefix is the part of a word that comes before the root. The prefix **un-** turns a word into its opposite. It turns *interesting* into *uninteresting*. *In-* is another prefix that does the same thing. It turns *sane* into *insane*. Note that *in-* changes to *im-* before the *m* sound. This makes it easier to say.

Change each of the words into its opposite by adding one of the following prefixes: *un-, in-,* or *im-*. Check each of your answers in a dictionary to be sure you have formed an actual word.

1. patriotic _____

2. remarkable _____

3. mature _____

4. affected _____

5. sufficient _____

6. complete _____

7. developed _____

8. persuasive _____

9. modest _____

10. sensitive _____

11. active _____

12. prepared _____

Passage

Read the passage. Then answer the questions that follow it.

A Life That Changed

Hans Christian Andersen's famous story "The Ugly Duckling" tells of a little duckling that looks different from others. The duckling is **mocked** for being odd. The little creature turns out not to be a duck at all but a beautiful swan. From a quick **glimpse** into the life of the author, we learn that a dramatic change took place in Andersen's own childhood. He also took a long time to fit in and to find a special place for himself.

Hans Christian Andersen was born in Denmark in 1805. His father was a shoemaker who struggled to make a living. Hans always felt loved by his parents. He had a happy childhood. He had no brothers or sisters. Andersen was a **sensitive** child who lived in a private world of his own. His greatest joy was a toy theater his father made for him. The little boy **entertained** his parents by putting on plays. He dressed the people of his little toy theater in **quaint** clothes that he made himself.

When Hans was eleven, his father died. The young boy's life changed **abruptly.** He had to go to work, but he failed at every job he **attempted.** His fellow workers could not understand the strange boy who spent all his time daydreaming. They treated him with **contempt,** making his life miserable. When he was fourteen, Hans **persuaded** his mother to let him go to the big city of Copenhagen. He tried to get work there as an actor, but was unsuccessful. He also tried dancing and singing, but he was not very good at these either. He tried writing plays, but theater owners **rejected** them. In this **phase** of his life, he didn't seem to fit in anywhere.

But Andersen **persisted** in his efforts to be a writer. Over the next fifteen years he wrote poems, travel articles, novels, and plays. He worked very hard, taking care to **revise** each sentence carefully until he got the words just right. No one paid much attention to his work, however, until he began writing fairy tales. He did not have to search for ideas for these; all he had to do was **recall** the stories his father had told him when he was a little boy. He wrote more than one hundred fifty wonderful fairy tales. **Achieving** fame at last, he became one of the best-loved writers in the world. You will read one of his stories in the next lesson.

abrupt
achieve
attempt
contempt
entertain
glimpse
mock
persist
persuade
phase
quaint
recall
reject
revise
sensitive

▶ **Answer each of the following questions in the form of a sentence. If a question does not contain a vocabulary word from the lesson's word list, use one in your answer. Use each word only once.**

1. How do you think a **sensitive** person like Andersen might have responded to cruel remarks?

   _____

   _____

2. What was one of Andersen's favorite childhood activities?

   _____

   _____

3. Why did the people in Hans's toy theater look so charmingly old-fashioned?

   _____

   _____

4. What caused an **abrupt** change in Andersen's life when he was a child?

   _____

   _____

5. What might Andersen have said to **persuade** his mother to let him go to Copenhagen?

   _____

   _____

6. Why must Andersen's mother have been pessimistic about his chances of success?

   _____

   _____

7. How do you know that Andersen was not popular with his fellow workers?

   _____

   _____

8. Was Andersen's playwriting successful?

_____

_____

9. What jobs did Hans try during the **phase** of his life when he didn't fit in anywhere?

_____

_____

10. What was Andersen's greatest **achievement?**

_____

_____

11. What helped give Andersen ideas for stories?

_____

_____

12. How can you tell that Andersen was usually not satisfied with his first version of a story?

_____

_____

13. What quality did Andersen have that helped him succeed?

_____

_____

14. Why do you think the people Andersen worked with **mocked** him?

_____

_____

15. Why might the story of the Ugly Duckling be of special interest to Andersen's readers?

_____

_____

FUN & FASCINATING FACTS

- The Latin *abruptus* means "broken" and forms the root of the adjective **abrupt.** If there is an *abrupt* end to something—a speech, for example—it means it was *broken* off suddenly and unexpectedly.

Other words formed from this root include *interrupt* (When you *interrupt* a conversation, you *break* into it) and *disrupt* (If you *disrupt* a meeting, you *break* it up).

Lesson **6**

For more practice and games, go to **www.WordlyWise3000.com**.

| **Word List** | Study the definitions of the words. Then do the exercises that follow. |

applaud
ə plôd´

v. To show approval, especially by clapping hands.
The audience **applauded** until the actors came back on stage to take another bow.

applause *n.* The showing of approval or enjoyment by cheering or clapping.
The theater lights came on after the **applause** had died down.

crafty
kraf´ tē

adj. Skilled at tricking others.
Templeton, the **crafty** and mean-spirited rat in *Charlotte's Web,* adds humor to the book.

disclose
dis klōz´

v. To make known.
The judge told the reporter she must **disclose** the names of those who attended the meeting.

drab
drab

adj. Dull and without color; not cheerful or colorful.
A sparrow is a **drab** little bird compared to a male cardinal.

entire
en tīr´

adj. Having nothing left out; whole; complete.
I recited the **entire** Robert Frost poem from memory.

exclaim
eks klām´

v. To speak suddenly and with strong feeling.
"Today was the worst day of my life!" she exclaimed.

exclamation (eks kləmā´ shən) *n.* A sharp cry of strong feeling.
Grandpa's **exclamation** of pain sent me rushing to his side.

exquisite
ek skwiz´ it

adj. Finely done or made; very beautiful.
The **exquisite** wood carvings on the museum door came from the island of Bali.

intend
in tend´

v. To plan; to have in mind.
I **intend** to give a piano recital on Monday.

intention *n.* An aim, plan, or purpose.
It was Thea's **intention** to open a bookstore, but she decided to go to engineering school instead.

jeer
jir

v. To speak or cry out in scorn; to mock.
My brother told me to ignore the older boys if they **jeered** when I sang.

n. Something said that is meant to hurt or insult.
An umpire soon learns to ignore the **jeers** of the crowd.

peer
pir

v. To look closely; to stare, especially at something that is hard to see or to understand.
Ahmed **peered** at the sign, trying to read what it said.

progress
prä´grəs

n. 1. Moving toward a goal.
The stormy sea slowed the small boat's **progress.**

2. An improvement.
I am finally making some **progress** mastering the new computer program.

v. (prə gres´) 1. To move forward.
Work on the new bridge **progressed** at a faster pace when the weather improved.

2. To advance to a higher stage; to improve.
Manuel **progressed** so fast on the tuba that he got into the school band.

refine
ri fīn´

v. To make pure by removing all unwanted matter.
We take oil from deep inside the earth and **refine** it into gasoline.

refined *adj.* 1. In a pure state.
Refined flour has a lot of the wheat germ removed.

2. Having good manners and good taste.
He was a noisy and rude boy, but as a young man he is gentle and **refined.**

scoundrel
skoun´drəl

n. A mean or wicked person.
Thank heavens the police caught the **scoundrel** who stole my wallet.

uneasy
un ē´zē

adj. Not comfortable; worried or nervous.
I felt **uneasy** walking down the dark street until I observed a police officer on the corner.

vain
vān

adj. 1. Having too high an opinion of one's looks or achievements.
Charlie is so **vain** he has a full-length mirror in every room.

2. Without success.
The firefighters made a **vain** attempt to keep the fire from spreading.

in vain *adv.* Without success or result; useless.
All my hand-waving was **in vain**—the teacher never called on me.

Choose two phrases to form a sentence that correctly uses a word from Word List 6. Write each sentence in the space provided.

1. (a) one that is complete.   (c) one that is not broken.
   (b) An entire set is   (d) An exquisite set is

   _____

   _____

2. (a) Crafty persons are those who (c) Vain persons are those who
   (b) think too highly of themselves. (d) do not think well of themselves.

   _____

   _____

3. (a) beautiful to look at.   (c) An exquisite fabric is one that is
   (b) A drab fabric is one that is (d) hidden from view.

   _____

   _____

4. (a) A jeer is   (c) a small hand tool.
   (b) A scoundrel is   (d) a dishonest person.

   _____

   _____

applaud
crafty
disclose
drab
entire
exclaim
exquisite
intend
jeer
peer
progress
refine
scoundrel
uneasy
vain

5. (a) easily hurt or upset.   (c) Refined people are
   (b) dull and uninteresting. (d) Drab colors are

   _____

   _____

6. (a) A crafty person is one who   (c) refuses to give up easily.
   (b) An uneasy person is one who   (d) is skilled at tricking people.

   _____

   _____

7. (a) An exclamation is   (c) something said with strong feeling.
   (b) An intention is   (d) a feeling of not being wanted.

   _____

   _____

8. (a) take it back.
   (b) To disclose something is to

   (c) To refine something is to
   (d) make it pure.

   _____

   _____

9. (a) An intention is something
   (b) one plans to do.

   (c) one denies having done.
   (d) A jeer is something

   _____

   _____

10. (a) come into view.
    (b) To peer is to

    (c) To progress is to
    (d) move forward.

    _____

    _____

11. (a) be hard to get along with.
    (b) To be applauded is to

    (c) To be uneasy is to
    (d) be worried or nervous.

    _____

    _____

Improve each of the following sentences by crossing out the bold phrase and replacing it with a word (or a form of the word) from Word List 6.

1. Josh **looked closely** at the faded sign but was unable to make out what it said.

2. Remi was eager to renew the contract, but all her efforts were **not met with success.**

3. A **well-mannered** person does not try to talk with his mouth full.

4. The **cruel and insensitive remarks** of his classmates did not dismay Carlos at all.

5. Icy road conditions slowed our **forward movement** through town.

6. "Now I understand!" Einstein **said suddenly, with strong feeling,** as he jumped up.

7. He was so **good at tricking people** that those he fooled did not even know it.

8. The inspector did not **let anyone know** the reason for her visit to the factory.

9. There was loud **cheering and clapping** when the members of the band came on stage.

applaud
crafty
disclose
drab
entire
exclaim
exquisite
intend
jeer
peer
progress
refine
scoundrel
uneasy
vain

Circle the letter or letters of each correct answer. A question may have more than one correct answer.

1. Which of the following might look **drab?**
   (a) a dirty suit
   (b) a rainbow
   (c) a colorfully painted room
   (d) a clown with orange hair

2. Which of the following are **entire** words?
   (a) father
   (b) m th r
   (c) s me b dy
   (d) I

3. Which of the following might be called **exquisite?**
   (a) a wedding dress
   (b) a diamond necklace
   (c) a grease spot
   (d) a trash can

4. What might cause **jeers** from the crowd at a baseball game?
   (a) an umpire's bad call
   (b) a great catch
   (c) a home run
   (d) a dropped catch

5. Which of the following might someone **peer** at?
   (a) a hard-to-read letter
   (b) a quaintly dressed person
   (c) a loud noise
   (d) an unpleasant smell

6. Which of the following might make a person **uneasy?**
   (a) winning first prize
   (b) hearing strange noises
   (c) climbing a tall ladder
   (d) being left alone at night

7. Which of the following would it be **vain** to attempt?
   (a) unscrambling an egg
   (b) learning Chinese
   (c) traveling backward in time
   (d) climbing Mount Everest

8. Which of the following would a person be likely to **applaud?**
   (a) a great achievement
   (b) a pessimistic remark
   (c) an entertaining show
   (d) a patriotic speech

Circle the two synonyms in each group of words.

1. recall	recite	reduce	remember
2. honest	uneasy	nervous	quaint
3. disclose	persuade	glimpse	reveal
4. hail	jeer	lack	mock
5. abrupt	sudden	severe	certain

Circle the two antonyms in each group of words.

6. complete	vain	modest	sufficient
7. crafty	exquisite	drab	forbidden
8. drowsy	crafty	honest	destructive
9. ease	contempt	respect	preparation
10. disclose	applaud	intend	jeer

applaud
crafty
disclose
drab
entire
exclaim
exquisite
intend
jeer
peer
progress
refine
scoundrel
uneasy
vain

Read the passage. Then answer the questions that follow it.

The Emperor's New Clothes*

Once there was an emperor who was very **vain.** He spent hour after hour **peering** at himself in the mirror. Whenever he got new clothes, he would gather his ministers around him so that they could tell him how wonderful he looked.

One day, two men came to see the emperor. They said they were master tailors. They told the emperor they could make him a suit of clothes so magnificent that everything else he owned would seem **drab.** The cloth would be so unusual that only those with the most **refined** taste would be able to see it. The emperor was foolish enough to believe them. He agreed to pay whatever they asked.

The "tailors" started work at once. Every day the emperor sent his ministers to check on their **progress.** Of course, they could see perfectly well that the **crafty** pair were only pretending to weave the cloth, and cut it, and stitch it. But they didn't dare **disclose** the truth to the emperor. Disagreeing with the emperor would be like confessing that they had poor taste. They felt **uneasy** about lying, but they believed they had no choice. They told the emperor only what he wanted to hear: that his new clothes were the most **exquisite** they had ever seen.

Finally the two **scoundrels** told the emperor that their work was complete. Excited by the news, the emperor announced that the next day would be a public holiday. He **intended** to walk through the streets of the town in his new clothes so that everyone could admire him. The next morning, the "tailors" carefully laid out the emperor's new clothes and helped him dress. The ministers gathered around to watch. And when at last the emperor stood proudly before them, turning this way and that, they forced out loud **exclamations** of delight. But of course the emperor was wearing only his underwear.

Meanwhile, officers of the palace guard had been up since before dawn. They were busy making sure that the townspeople turned out to **applaud** the emperor as he went by. Now the **entire** town lined the streets to see him. Under the watchful eyes of the officers, the people cheered and waved flags. The emperor loved every minute of it. But then something unexpected

* This passge is a retelling of the popular fairy tale by Hans Christian Andersen.

happened. Above the roar of the crowd, the emperor heard a child's voice. A little boy shouted, "Look! The emperor has no clothes!" The cry was at once taken up by the crowd. "THE EMPEROR HAS NO CLOTHES! THE EMPEROR HAS NO CLOTHES!"

The emperor looked down at himself and saw that it was true. He knew that he had been tricked. Feeling very foolish, he ran back to the palace as fast as he could, the **jeers** of the crowd ringing in his ears.

▶ **Answer each of the following questions in the form of a sentence. If a question does not contain a vocabulary word from the lesson's word list, use one in your answer. Use each word only once.**

1. What did the emperor do with his time?

   _____

   _____

2. Why might the emperor have been tempted to get rid of all his old clothes after he talked to his tailors?

   _____

   _____

3. How would you describe **refined** taste?

   _____

   _____

4. Why was it impossible to judge how the tailors' work was **progressing?**

   _____

   _____

5. Why does the passage refer to the two tailors as **scoundrels?**

   _____

   _____

6. Who finally **disclosed** the truth to the emperor?

   _____

   _____

applaud
crafty
disclose
drab
entire
exclaim
exquisite
intend
jeer
peer
progress
refine
scoundrel
uneasy
vain

7. Why were the ministers **uneasy?**

_____

_____

8. What did the ministers tell the emperor?

_____

_____

9. What do you think the ministers thought of the two tailors?

_____

_____

10. What do you think was the tailors' **intention** in tricking the emperor?

_____

_____

11. Why did the ministers **exclaim** in delight?

_____

_____

12. Why do you think the child might have deserved the crowd's **applause?**

_____

_____

13. Why did the **entire** town show up to see the emperor?

_____

_____

14. Why did the emperor run back to the palace?

_____

_____

15. What vocabulary word describes the emperor perfectly? Why?

_____

_____

- The adjective **drab** is also the name of a color — a light, green-brown. (U.S. soldiers wear olive-*drab* clothing.) *Drab* is also a noun meaning "a small amount," but it is found only in the phrase "in dribs and drabs," meaning a little bit at a time. (Instead of paying me the money all at once, they gave it to me *in dribs and drabs*.)

- **Vain** and *vein* are homophones. They sound alike but have different meanings and spellings. A *vein* is a blood vessel that carries blood to the heart.

- As well as being a verb, **peer** is also a noun. It means "an equal; a person of the same rank or position as another." For example, "Those sixth graders are my *peers*. We all are in the same class." Or, to say that Daniel Webster had no *peer* as a public speaker is to say that no one could equal him in the art of public speaking. A *peer* is also the name for a member of the British House of Lords.

Like *vain* and *vein,* note that **peer** and *pier* are homophones.

applaud

crafty

disclose

drab

entire

exclaim

exquisite

intend

jeer

peer

progress

refine

scoundrel

uneasy

vain

Lesson 7

Study the definitions of the words. Then do the exercises that follow.

alter
ôl´ tər

v. To change in some way; to make or become different.
Let's **alter** our uniforms so they will fit better.

alteration *n.* A change.
Please don't make any **alterations** in my newspaper column.

confuse
kən fyo͞oz´

v. 1. To make or become unclear or mixed up in the mind.
That math problem totally **confused** me.

2. To mistake one person or thing for another.
I always **confuse** Sally with her twin sister Samantha.

confusing *adj.* Hard to follow or understand; unclear.
The play was **confusing** at first, but I began to understand it in the second act.

confusion *n.* A state of disorder.
After the playoff game, the dressing room was total **confusion.**

distribute
di strib´ yoot

v. 1. To give out; to divide among several or many.
Ahmed **distributed** programs before the concert.

2. To be spread over.
Small parks are **distributed** throughout London.

eject
i jekt´

v. To force or throw out.
When the seventh graders refused to listen, the coach **ejected** them from the team meeting.

embrace
im brās´

v. 1. To hold closely in one's arms; to hug.
My parents **embraced** me when I got off the plane.

2. To take up seriously.
We **embraced** the idea of smaller classes, but lacked the teachers to carry it out.

n. A hug.
At the end of the movie, the hero and the heroine were locked in an **embrace.**

equip i kwip´	*v.* To provide with what is needed. All new cars now come **equipped** with airbags. **equipment** *n.* Things that are needed for some activity. Sarah bought all her camping **equipment** at yard sales.
flexible flek´ sə bəl	*adj.* 1. Able to bend easily. Dancers and gymnasts have very **flexible** bodies. 2. Able to adjust to new or different situations. Antonio is so **flexible** he can get along with anyone.
instant in´ stənt	*n.* A moment; a very short period of time. It took Luis only an **instant** to calculate the amount of paint we would need. *adj.* Happening or done at once; quick. He gave an **instant** "yes" to her offer.
keen kēn	*adj.* 1. Having a sharp edge. The **keen** blade of the knife sliced through the thick rope with ease. 2. Showing a strong interest; eager. Marta signed up for lessons because she was **keen** to learn to play the guitar. 3. Having sharp senses; quick to understand. With her **keen** mind, she was able to master physics with ease.
limp limp	*v.* To walk lamely or in an uneven way. I **limped** for two weeks after I fell on the ice. *n.* An uneven or lopsided walk. She walked very fast, in spite of her **limp.** *adj.* Not stiff or firm. His handshake was as **limp** as a wet rag.
scurry skʉr´ ē	*v.* To move quickly, with rapid little steps. The chipmunk **scurried** up the tree as we approached.
seize sēz	*v.* 1. To grasp suddenly; to grab hold of. He **seized** my hand and begged me not to go. 2. To take by force of the law. The government can **seize** many of the things you own if you do not pay your taxes.

shallow	*adj.* 1. Not deep.
sha´lō	We went wading in a **shallow** stream.
	2. With little seriousness or deep thought.
	He tried to sound intelligent, but his arguments were really quite **shallow.**

surround	*v.* To enclose on all sides.
sə round´	The prison was **surrounded** by a high fence.
	surroundings *n. pl.* The things or conditions around a person or place.
	The hotel's peaceful **surroundings** made it a perfect place to relax.

| victim | *n.* One who is hurt, killed, or suffers. |
| vik´ təm | The scoundrel tried to deny that he had cheated his **victims** of their life savings. |

7A ▷ Finding Meanings

Choose two phrases to form a sentence that correctly uses a word from Word List 7. Write each sentence in the space provided.

1. (a) Surroundings are   (c) needed items for some activity.
   (b) Alterations are   (d) the conditions around one.

   _____

   _____

2. (a) To eject a group is to   (c) To equip a group is to
   (b) provide it with what is needed. (d) allow it to take part.

   _____

   _____

3. (a) throw them out.   (c) take them by force.
   (b) To seize papers is to   (d) To distribute papers is to

   _____

   _____

4. (a) To be flexible is to be   (c) unwilling to change your mind.
   (b) To be keen is to be   (d) agreeable to any sudden change of plan.

_____

_____

5. (a) Alteration is   (c) a state of being mixed up.
   (b) unwillingness to change.   (d) Confusion is

_____

_____

6. (a) Victims are   (c) persons who avoid injury.
   (b) persons who are hurt.   (d) Embraces are

_____

_____

7. (a) A flexible person   (c) A keen person
   (b) is one who is eager.   (d) is one who is vain.

_____

_____

8. (a) a hug.   (c) An instant is
   (b) An embrace is   (d) a handshake.

_____

_____

9. (a) To limp is to   (c) To scurry is to
   (b) grasp firmly.   (d) walk unevenly.

_____

_____

10. (a) to hold onto them.   (c) To distribute things is
    (b) to give them out.   (d) To confuse things is

_____

_____

alter
confuse
distribute
eject
embrace
equip
flexible
instant
keen
limp
scurry
seize
shallow
surround
victim

Improve each of the following sentences by crossing out the bold phrase and replacing it with a word (or a form of the word) from Word List 7.

1. The dog's **uneven walk** was caused by a thorn in its left front paw.

2. I **opened my arms and held** my cousin, whom I hadn't seen in two years.

3. Stay close to shore where the water is **not very deep.**

4. My cat jumped as a mouse **ran with quick little steps** across the kitchen floor.

5. I caught a glimpse of the president in the parade for just one **very short period of time.**

6. This map is very **hard to follow** because some of the streets aren't named.

7. With just a slight **change in form** of the shape of the number, a 3 becomes an 8.

8. The boxes of food were **given out** in time for Thanksgiving.

9. My whole family **gathered around me,** singing "Happy Birthday."

10. Luckily, the pilot was **thrown with great force** from the plane before it crashed.

Circle the letter or letters of each correct answer. A question may have more than one correct answer.

1. Which of the following can be **altered?**
   (a) one's plans
   (b) today's date
   (c) a dress's hemline
   (d) one's age

2. Which of the following are **flexible?**
   (a) a sewing needle
   (b) a garden hose
   (c) a dancer's body
   (d) a length of cooked spaghetti

3. Which of the following could be given in an **instant?**
   (a) a yes-or-no answer
   (b) a nod of agreement
   (c) a ten-page report
   (d) a smile of welcome

4. Which of the following might feel **limp?**
   (a) a sheet of wet cardboard
   (b) a sleeping child
   (c) a sheet of ice
   (d) a sheet of plywood

5. Which of the following could **scurry?**
   (a) a spider
   (b) a whale
   (c) an elephant
   (d) a mouse

6. Which of the following could be **seized?**
   (a) a person's arm
   (b) a person's boat
   (c) a sneeze
   (d) a puff of smoke

7. Which of the following could be **shallow?**
   (a) a stick
   (b) a tree
   (c) a person's thinking
   (d) a pond

8. Which of the following might be **keen?**
   (a) a pessimist
   (b) a razor blade
   (c) a hammer
   (d) a dog's hearing

alter
confuse
distribute
eject
embrace
equip
flexible
instant
keen
limp
scurry
seize
shallow
surround
victim

In Lesson 5, you met three prefixes, *un-, in-,* and *im-.* When attached to the front of a word, they turned the word into its opposite. The meaning of each prefix is "not."

Here are three more prefixes. They add to, or change the meaning of, the word they're attached to. *Pre-* adds the meaning "before," *re-* adds the meaning "again" or "against," and *ex-* adds the meaning "out." The prefix *ex-* is sometimes shortened to *e-*.

In column three, write the prefix of each word listed in column two. In the space provided, write the meaning of that prefix.

Definition	Word	Prefix
1. to fight against	resist	_____
Prefix Meaning _____		
2. to bring out into the open	expose	_____
Prefix Meaning _____		
3. to act before the need arises	prepare	_____
Prefix Meaning _____		
4. not feeling easy in one's mind	uneasy	_____
Prefix Meaning _____		
5. to bring to mind once again	recall	_____
Prefix Meaning _____		
6. to go out of bounds	exceed	_____
Prefix Meaning _____		
7. to go over to correct	revise	_____
Prefix Meaning _____		
8. to speak out loudly	exclaim	_____
Prefix Meaning _____		

9. to throw out   eject   _____

    Prefix Meaning _____

10. to say over again what one   recite   _____

    Prefix Meaning _____

Passage

Read the passage. Then answer the questions that follow it.

Armed But Not Dangerous

What has one head, eight arms, and the ability to change from gray to green to brown? Here is a clue: the Greek word for eight is *okto*. If you guessed octopus, you're right!

The octopus lives in holes or openings in the rocky bottom of the sea. It protects itself from enemies by changing color to match its **surroundings.** In seaweed it can turn green; on sand it can turn brown; against rocks it can turn gray. For example, suppose an octopus is attacked by a shark. In an **instant,** it can change its color to blend into the background. The surprised shark is left wondering where the octopus went. The octopus can also protect itself by **ejecting** a large blob of black ink-like liquid. This acts as a screen. The trick can **confuse** the attacker into going after the blob. Meanwhile, the octopus has a chance to slip away.

An octopus has no bones, so it can easily **alter** its shape; it can then force its way inside empty shells or under rocks or into very narrow openings. To be even safer, it may cover itself with stones or shells.

The octopus's eight rubbery arms are very **flexible.** They can easily wrap around even quite small objects. Each arm is **equipped** with two rows of fleshy, deeply set suckers. These give it a powerful grip. The octopus uses its arms to **seize** other animals as they **scurry** along the sea floor. Crabs and lobsters are among its **victims.** The octopus uses the two strong, horny beaks in its mouth to crack open their shells.

The octopus has **keen** eyesight. It needs sharp eyes because it hunts mostly at night. It has a large brain for its size, and it makes full use of its intelligence to catch food. For example, if an octopus cannot open a clam,

alter
confuse
distribute
eject
embrace
equip
flexible
instant
keen
limp
scurry
seize
shallow
surround
victim

it will wait until the clam opens itself. When it does, the octopus will put a stone between the two shells so that they cannot close. Then it can get at the juicy clam without having to struggle.

There are many different kinds of octopuses, and they are widely **distributed** throughout the world's oceans. They live mostly in warm, **shallow** water, not far from shore. The smallest ones grow to be no more than two inches across. The largest ones live in the Pacific Ocean. They can grow to be thirty feet across. Their width is mainly in their arms; their bodies might be only eighteen inches.

If, when swimming in the Pacific, you venture too far from shore, you may find yourself in the **embrace** of an octopus. What should you do? It is best not to struggle. Just let your body go **limp;** the octopus will probably let you go. Although movies sometimes show them as terrifying and dangerous monsters, there is no reason to fear them. Around humans, at least, octopuses are usually shy and gentle creatures.

Answer each of the following questions in the form of a sentence. If a question does not contain a vocabulary word from the lesson's word list, use one in your answer. Use each word only once.

1. Why does an octopus sitting in seaweed turn green?

_____

_____

2. How long does it take for an octopus to change colors?

_____

_____

3. Why does the octopus make a "screen"?

_____

_____

4. How does it make this screen?

_____

_____

5. How does its lack of a skeleton benefit an octopus?

_____

_____

6. How would bones in an octopus's arms affect the way it uses them?

_____

_____

7. How is the octopus **equipped** to grip things?

_____

_____

8. How do its eight arms help an octopus obtain food?

_____

_____

9. Why might an approaching octopus cause a crab to start **scurrying?**

_____

_____

10. How does an octopus get at the meat in a lobster it has caught?

_____

_____

11. Which of the octopus's senses is especially well-developed?

_____

_____

12. In what parts of the world do octopuses live?

_____

_____

13. Why are you unlikely to see an octopus in the middle of the Atlantic Ocean?

_____

_____

alter
confuse
distribute
eject
embrace
equip
flexible
instant
keen
limp
scurry
seize
shallow
surround
victim

14. Would you be in danger in an octopus's **embrace?** Explain.

_____

_____

15. What is the meaning of **limp,** as used in the passage?

_____

_____

FUN & FASCINATING FACTS

- **Flexible** means "able to bend or change easily." The antonym of *flexible* is *rigid,* which means "stiff" or "unbending." An iron bar is rigid; if it is heated until it becomes very hot, it becomes flexible. Both words can be used *literally,* as in the example of the iron bar, and *figuratively,* as in the following examples: A person willing to change plans at the last minute is said to be *flexible;* someone refusing to make such changes may be called *rigid.* A job with *rigid* hours is one in which the work hours cannot be changed; a job with *flexible* hours is one in which the hours can be changed easily to suit the needs of the worker.

- **Alter** is a verb; *altar* (with two *a*'s) is a noun. An *altar* is a table or platform used in churches or temples as a center of worship. A bride and groom may kneel or stand before the altar when they get married. *Alter* and *altar* are homophones—words that sound alike but have different meanings and spellings.

For more practice and games, go to **www.WordlyWise3000.com**.

Word List | Study the definitions of the words. Then do the exercises that follow.

---

ancient
ān´ chənt

adj. Very old; of a long time ago.
The **ancient** city of Carthage was destroyed by the Romans in 146 B.C.E.

---

century
sen´ chər ē

n. A period of one hundred years.
The twenty-first **century** began on January 1, 2001.

---

chamber
chām´ bər

n. A room.
The queen always has breakfast in her **chamber** before she comes downstairs.

chambers *n. pl.* An office or group of offices.
Lawyers for both sides met in the judge's **chambers**.

---

descend
di send´

v. To go or come down.
The plane slowly **descended** to 2,000 feet.

descendant *n.* One who has certain persons as one's parents, grandparents, etc.
The writer Alex Haley was a **descendant** of Kunta Kinte, who was brought to America as a slave from West Africa in 1767.

---

entry
en´ trē

n. 1. A way in.
The thieves gained **entry** through an unlocked window.

2. Each separate item in a diary or list.
The next **entry** in her diary simply said, "My brother returned home today after a long absence."

---

interior
in tir´ ē ər

n. The inside part of something.
The sun's **interior** is about 150,000 times hotter than boiling water.

adj. Having to do with the inside part.
Interior doors do not have to be as strongly made as front or back doors.

---

intrude
in trōōd´

v. To come or go in without permission or welcome.
I didn't mean to **intrude** on you while you were working.

intrusion *n.* The act of intruding.
"Forgive my **intrusion**," she said as she came in without knocking.

intruder *n.* One who intrudes.
People were so unfriendly that I felt like an **intruder** at Jeff's party.

---

locate
lō´ kāt

v. 1. To find.
Marta **located** the missing books in less than an hour.

2. To put or to be found in a place.
We're going to **locate** our office across the street from the school.

location (lō kā´ shən) *n.* The place where something can be found.
Will you please give me the **location** of the nearest post office?

passage
pa´ sij

n. 1. A part of a written work or piece of music.
The final **passage** of the Mozart mass brought tears to the audience's eyes.

2. The act or process of passing, as through time or from place to place.
His deeply lined face clearly showed the **passage** of time.

3. A way through which to pass.
Leon's room was at the end of a long, dimly lit **passage.**

portion
pôr´ shən

n. 1. A part or share of the whole.
I got the first **portion** of my allowance last week.

2. A serving or helping, as of food.
My diet recommends a four-ounce **portion** of fish or chicken once a day.

precious
pre´ shəs

adj. 1. Very valuable.
The necklace was made of diamonds, emeralds, and other **precious** stones.

2. Much loved.
She tried in vain to save her **precious** books from the fire.

quarry
kwôr´ ē

n. 1. A deep pit where stone is cut out of the ground.
The marble for these tiles came from a **quarry** in Vermont.

2. An animal that is being hunted.
The hunters gave up the chase when they lost sight of their **quarry.**

ramp
ramp

n. A slanted walk or roadway that connects a lower to a higher place.
The law says that there has to be a **ramp** for those who cannot use the steps.

spacious
spā´ shəs

adj. Having lots of room.
The **spacious** kitchen had room for a large round table that seated eight.

surface	*n.* 1. The outside layer; the top.
sŭr´fəs	The **surface** of the moon is covered with craters.

2. An outward look or appearance.
He seemed cheerful on the **surface,** but I knew how miserable he must have felt to be so cold and wet.

v. To rise to the top of a body of water.
The latest submarines can stay underwater for weeks before they need to **surface.**

8A Finding Meanings

Choose two phrases to form a sentence that correctly uses a word from Word List 8. Write each sentence in the space provided.

1. (a) Interior walls are
   (b) those on the inside.
   (c) those that surround a private area.
   (d) Ancient walls are

   _____

   _____

2. (a) The passage of something is
   (b) The surface of something is
   (c) its outward appearance.
   (d) its innermost part.

   _____

   _____

3. (a) A spacious city is one
   (b) that has many visitors.
   (c) that is very old.
   (d) An ancient city is one

   _____

   _____

4. (a) A passage is
   (b) a free pass to a public event.
   (c) An intrusion is
   (d) a way through which to go.

   _____

   _____

ancient
century
chamber
descend
entry
interior
intrude
locate
passage
portion
precious
quarry
ramp
spacious
surface

5. (a) Something that is spacious   (c) is very valuable.
   (b) Something that is precious   (d) seems true but is actually false.

   _____

   _____

6. (a) a sloping walkway.   (c) A ramp is
   (b) A quarry is   (d) a contest.

   _____

   _____

7. (a) an unwelcome arrival.   (c) A location is
   (b) a serving of food.   (d) An intrusion is

   _____

   _____

8. (a) A portion is   (c) a pit from which stone is cut.
   (b) A quarry is   (d) a building open to the public.

   _____

   _____

9. (a) To locate the stairs is   (c) to go up them.
   (b) to go down them.   (d) To descend the stairs is

   _____

   _____

10. (a) A portion is   (c) a large room.
    (b) A chamber is   (d) the topmost part.

    _____

    _____

Improve each of the following sentences by crossing out the bold phrase and replacing it with a word (or a form of the word) from Word List 8.

1. Our new apartment has a closet that is **very large,** with room enough to hold a fold-up bed.

2. The United States has enough coal to last for at least a **period of one hundred years.**

3. The divers were searching for the **exact spot** of the sunken treasure.

4. To enter the parking garage you have to drive up the **sloping way** leading to a higher level.

5. The lion's **intended victim** was a young antelope.

6. As we approached the clubhouse, we saw that the only **way in** was blocked by a huge pile of snow.

7. Angela told me she would pay back a **part of the total amount** of the money she owed me by next week.

8. These are the **group of offices** where Senate hearings are held.

9. The **process of passing** of time could be seen in the crumbling stone buildings and rutted streets.

10. A large bullfrog suddenly **rose to the top of the water** and landed on a lilypad.

ancient
century
chamber
descend
entry
interior
intrude
locate
passage
portion
precious
quarry
ramp
spacious
surface

Circle the letter or letters of each correct answer. A question may have more than one correct answer.

1. Which of the following might be thought of as **precious?**
   (a) a child
   (b) freedom of speech
   (c) a diamond ring
   (d) chewing gum stuck to your shoe

2. Which of the following is **ancient?**
   (a) a joke you've heard before
   (b) last year's calendar
   (c) an Egyptian mummy
   (d) a dinosaur bone

3. Which of the following might an **intruder** at a private meeting be asked to do?
   (a) help give out the notes
   (b) join in the talk
   (c) leave immediately
   (d) meet the other people

4. Which of the following might a person try to **locate?**
   (a) a problem with a car's engine
   (b) the city of New York on a map
   (c) a missing relative
   (d) a secret

5. Which of the following might you ask for a **portion** of?
   (a) a friend's jacket
   (b) the Sunday newspaper
   (c) cole slaw
   (d) a friend's age

6. Which of the following has an **interior?**
   (a) a planet
   (b) a sheet of paper
   (c) a house
   (d) a car

7. Which of the following can be measured in **centuries?**
   (a) the age of the United States
   (b) the size of the United States
   (c) time
   (d) space

8. Which of the following has a **surface?**
   (a) a sharp pain
   (b) a coat of paint
   (c) a lake
   (d) the sun

Write the synonym of each word on the left on the line next to it. Choose from the words on the right, which are in a different order.

1. spacious _____ valuable

2. precious _____ old

3. keen _____ grasp

4. ancient _____ improve

5. applaud _____ change

6. locate _____ eager

7. alter _____ roomy

8. seize _____ hug

9. embrace _____ cheer

10. progress _____ find

ancient
century
chamber
descend
entry
interior
intrude
locate
passage
portion
precious
quarry
ramp
spacious
surface

8E ▷ Passage

Read the passage. Then answer the questions that follow it.

The Great Pyramid

Over two thousand years ago, a Greek writer named Antipater made a list of what he called the Seven Wonders of the World. Only one of those **ancient** sights remains today. It is the Great Pyramid, in Egypt.

The Great Pyramid is **located** just outside Cairo. It was built by one of the earliest kings of Egypt, Cheops. Cheops intended this pyramid to be a tomb, or burial place, for himself. It covers an area bigger than one hundred football fields and stands 450 feet high. It is the largest of the more than sixty pyramids in Egypt. The Great Pyramid is made of two and a half million blocks of stone; some of them weigh as much as fifteen tons. The pyramid's **surface** was once covered in shining white limestone and was perfectly smooth. Over the **centuries,** most of this outside layer has been stripped away; very little of it is left.

It may have taken as long as twenty years to build the Great Pyramid. The stone for the great blocks came from nearby. The white limestone for the outside came from **quarries** near the Nile River. The blocks were floated across on rafts. They were then dragged up a **ramp** of earth. The ramp was built up in stages as the work progressed. Skilled stonecutters worked all year on the pyramid. Other work was done by farmers, who worked for a **portion** of each year. The farmers probably worked from July to October, when the Nile overflowed its banks and flooded the fields. Workers believed that their king, Cheops, was a god, a **descendant** of the sun god Ra. They felt he deserved this magnificent tomb.

The **interior** of the Great Pyramid contains many rooms. The rooms are connected by **passages** leading to the outside. King Cheops was laid to rest in one of the most **spacious** rooms. The Egyptians believed in a life after death. They left food and drink with the king's body as well as many **precious** objects he had used in daily life. The Egyptians believed he would need these in the next world.

The **chamber** in which the dead king lay was closed off with huge granite slabs. The Egyptians wanted to be sure that people could not gain **entry** to the room. In spite of this, however, **intruders** later found a way in. They stole the gold objects and the jewels that were inside. They even made off with the body! The Great Pyramid failed to keep Cheops's body safe, but it has kept his name alive over 4,500 years after his death.

▶ **Answer each of the following questions in the form of a sentence. If a question does not contain a vocabulary word from the lesson's word list, use one in your answer. Use each word only once.**

1. What makes the Great Pyramid unusual among the places on Antipater's list?

_____

_____

2. How could one go from room to room within the Great Pyramid?

_____

_____

3. Why would the **interior** of the Great Pyramid be very dark?

_____

_____

4. How did the Egyptians raise the stones onto the pyramid?

_____

_____

5. Why did the white limestone have to come by water?

_____

_____

6. Why did some people work on the pyramid for only a **portion** of the year?

_____

_____

ancient

century

chamber

descend

entry

interior

intrude

locate

passage

portion

precious

quarry

ramp

spacious

surface

7. How does the room where the king's body was placed compare with other rooms?

_____

_____

8. Why do you think the passage refers to the king's room as a **chamber?**

_____

_____

9. What are some of the **precious** objects that might have been left with the dead king?

_____

_____

10. Why did the Egyptians place granite slabs outside the king's tomb?

_____

_____

11. What happened to the gold and the jewels that were inside the tomb?

_____

_____

12. When (to the nearest hundred years) was the Great Pyramid built?

_____

_____

13. Why did the Egyptians think Cheops deserved such a magnificent tomb?

_____

_____

14. How does the Great Pyramid differ from when it was first built?

_____

_____

15. What is the **location** of Cairo?

_____

_____

ancient
century
chamber
descend
entry
interior
intrude
locate
passage
portion
precious
quarry
ramp
spacious
surface

- In Lesson 7 you learned that the Greek word for "eight" is *okto*. In Latin, it became *octo*. (An *octopus* has eight arms. *October* was the eighth month in the Roman calendar; we changed it and made it the tenth month.)

- A large number of English words are formed from Greek or Latin numbers. Among them is our word **century,** a period of one hundred years. It comes from the Latin for one hundred, which is *centum*. Other words sharing this root include *cent* (there are one hundred cents in a dollar), *centipede* (this creature was once thought to have one hundred legs, but it actually has about seventy), and *centimeter* (there are one hundred centimeters in a meter).

In 1976 the United States celebrated its *bicentennial*. If you knew nothing of the history of the United States, but knew that the Latin for "two" is *bi*, could you figure out how old the United States was in 1976?

- How can the word **quarry** have two such separate and unrelated meanings? For the answer to this question, we must look into the word's history. In fact, it is not one word but two quite different ones that by chance have the same spelling.

The word for an animal being hunted comes from the old French *cuiree*, the name for body parts fed to animals after a successful hunt. The word passed into English as *querre*, which in modern English became *quarry*.

The word for a deep pit where stone is cut out of the ground comes from the Latin *quadrum*, which means "squared at the corners." It was applied to stones used for building, which were usually squared at the corners. As the word changed over the years to *quarry*, it came to mean the place from which the stone was obtained.

Crossword Puzzle   Solve the crossword puzzle by studying the clues and filling in the answer boxes. Clues followed by a number are definitions of vocabulary words in lessons 5 through 8. The number gives the lesson from which the answer to the clue is taken.

Clues Across

1. To give out (7)
5. To win over by arguing or asking (5)
8. To change in some way (7)
9. An animal that is being hunted (8)
10. The topmost part; the outer layer (8)
11. A part or share of the whole (8)
12. Twice as much
14. Each separate item on a list (8)
15. Skilled at tricking others (6)
17. Dull and without color (6)
19. Adam and _____
21. To make pure (6)
23. To take by force of the law (7)
25. Eight, _____ , ten
26. A large room (8)
27. Having nothing left out (6)
28. Place where something is (8)

Clues Down

2. To be around on all sides (7)
3. To remember (5)
4. To interest and amuse (5)
5. To go on longer than expected (5)
6. Opposite of *open*
7. Happening suddenly without warning (5)
12. To go to a lower level (8)
13. To hold closely (7)
14. Used to see with
16. Opposite of *no*
18. To say you won't accept (5)
20. Very strict or harsh
22. To throw out (7)
24. Showing a strong interest; eager (7)

Lesson 9

For more practice and games, go to **www.WordlyWise3000.com**.

| **Word List** | Study the definitions of the words. Then do the exercises that follow. |

advantage
əd van´ tij

n. Something that is helpful or useful.
It is an **advantage** to be able to speak French when visiting Paris.

take advantage of   *v.* To make use of; to benefit oneself by treating others unfairly.
Martina **took advantage of** her position as camp leader by giving all the best jobs to her friends.

astonish
əstä´ nish

v. To surprise or amaze.
It **astonished** me to discover that my new friend and I were born on the same day in the same town.

astonishment   *n.* Great surprise or amazement.
The children watched in **astonishment** as the magician pulled a rabbit out of a hat.

confirm
kén férm´

v. 1. To show or prove to be true.
Before giving me a library card, the librarian asked me to **confirm** my street address by showing a copy of my phone bill.

2. To approve or give one's agreement to.
The members of Congress vote to **confirm** the appointment of Supreme Court judges.

distant
dis´ tənt

adj. 1. Very far away in time.
Space travel in the very **distant** future may involve journeys to the stars.

2. Very far away; not near or close by.
Marco Polo's travels took him to many **distant** lands.

distance   *n.* The length of the space between two places.
The **distance** between Deneen's home and her school was exactly one mile.

founder
faün´ dər

n. A person who sets up something that lasts.
George Washington and Thomas Jefferson are two of the **founders** of our nation.

v. To sink below the surface of the water.
The ship struck a rock and **foundered** before a rescue team could reach it.

hamlet
ham´ lət

n. A small village.
A single street ran through the **hamlet,** which had one church, a general store, and about a hundred houses.

host
hōst

n. 1. A large number.
Graceland is visited by **hosts** of people from all over the world who come to see the house where Elvis Presley lived.

2. One who greets and entertains guests and takes care of their needs at a party or restaurant.
The guests said goodbye to their **host** and thanked him for a lovely New Year's Eve party.

misgiving
mis giv´ ing

n. A feeling of doubt, uncertainty, or concern about what may happen in the future.
If Ellen had any **misgivings** about joining the group, she gave no sign of it.

parch
pärch

v. To make or become very dry.
The sun **parched** the fields and made the grass turn brown.

parched (pärcht) *adj.* Lacking water; thirsty.
We didn't take enough water with us, and we were **parched** before we came to the end of our walk.

prospect
präs´ pekt

n. Something that is waited for, expected, or hoped for.
All the hotels were full, and there seemed little **prospect** of our finding a place to spend the night.

v. To look in the ground for valuable metals like gold and silver.
The four men camped alongside the river told us they were **prospecting** for gold.

prospector *n.* A person who explores an area to look for valuable metals.
The **prospector** let out a whoop of joy when he saw some shiny yellow objects lying on the riverbank.

scarce
skers

adj. In short supply; not plentiful.
When gasoline is **scarce,** the price goes up.

scarcity (sker´ sət ē) *n.* A shortage.
Due to the **scarcity** of candles in the store when the hurricane struck, customers were allowed only two each.

shrewd
shrüd

adj. Clever; good at understanding what is needed and acting on it.
A **shrewd** lawyer prepares her client to answer questions she knows the client will be asked in court.

sole sōl	*adj.* Being the only one of its kind; belonging to only one person or group. After her husband died, Mrs. Mazoor became the **sole** owner of the toy store. *n.* 1. The bottom surface of the foot or of a shoe or boot. Shoes with leather **soles** usually cost more than those made of plastic. 2. A flat fish that is caught and eaten for food. Grilled **sole** is a popular item on the seafood restaurant's menu.
torment tôr´ ment	*n.* Great pain or suffering. I cannot imagine the **torment** suffered by a wild animal caught in a steel trap. (tôr ment´) *v.* To cause pain or suffering. The thought that she might have been the cause of the accident **tormented** the driver of the car.
typical tip´ i kəl	*adj.* Being like others of its kind. A **typical** home in this area has three bedrooms, a kitchen, a living room, and one bathroom.

9A ▶ Finding Meanings

advantage
astonish
confirm
distant
founder
hamlet
host
misgiving
parch
prospect
scarce
shrewd
sole
torment
typical

Choose two phrases to form a sentence that correctly uses a word from Word List 9. Write each sentence in the space provided.

1. (a) A hamlet is
   (b) a small village.
   (c) An advantage is
   (d) a large number.

_____

_____

2. (a) is to hurt that person.
   (b) To torment someone
   (c) is to care for that person.
   (d) To astonish someone

_____

_____

3. (a) A typical city
   (b) is one that is very old.
   (c) is one that is far away.
   (d) A distant city

_____

_____

4. (a) the only one of its kind.   (c) A founder is
   (b) A sole is   (d) a flat fish used for food.

_____

_____

5. (a) A shrewd plan   (c) is one that is cleverly thought out.
   (b) is one that is kept secret.   (d) A typical plan

_____

_____

6. (a) To astonish someone   (c) To confirm someone
   (b) is to get rid of that person.   (d) is to approve that person's
      appointment.

_____

_____

7. (a) doubts about the future.   (c) Advantages are
   (b) unwanted gifts.   (d) Misgivings are

_____

_____

8. (a) To founder is to   (c) To prospect is to
   (b) sink below the surface.   (d) start over.

_____

_____

9. (a) very thirsty.   (c) To be parched is to be
   (b) To be scarce is to be   (d) not wanted or needed.

_____

_____

10. (a) To take advantage of someone   (c) To astonish someone
    (b) is to amaze that person.   (d) is to dislike that person.

_____

_____

Improve each of the following sentences by crossing out the bold phrase and replacing it with a word (or a form of the word) from Word List 9.

1. The **length of an imaginary line** from Earth to the moon is about a quarter of a million miles.

2. The hot sun had **taken every drop of moisture out of** the soil so that nothing grew.

3. Being tall is a great **helpful thing that can make all the difference** to a basketball player.

4. After twenty-two miles, Asad was the **one and only** runner left in the race.

5. Simon was very **good at knowing what to do in every situation,** and he managed to cause trouble for others without ever getting into trouble himself.

6. Mr. Bullwhistle is the **person who was the first owner** of this company.

7. Blankets were **in short supply, without enough to go around,** so some campers got one and some got none.

8. Today's weather was **just like it usually is** on the island: it rained in the morning and poured in the afternoon.

9. A **very large number** of people came together in the park to celebrate Earth Day.

10. Baby Alice was busy **being cruel and causing pain to** the cat by pulling its tail.

advantage
astonish
confirm
distant
founder
hamlet
host
misgiving
parch
prospect
scarce
shrewd
sole
torment
typical

Circle the letter or letters of each correct answer. A question may have more than one correct answer.

1. Which of the following could cause **torment?**
   - (a) a bad sunburn
   - (b) a broken shoelace
   - (c) looking at the moon
   - (d) scoring the winning goal

2. Which of the following has a **sole?**
   - (a) a fish
   - (b) a foot
   - (c) a boot
   - (d) a shoe

3. Which of the following might affect a person's **prospects** for getting into college?
   - (a) red hair
   - (b) leadership qualities
   - (c) poor grades
   - (d) ability at sports

4. Which of the following could easily be taken **advantage** of?
   - (a) a weak person
   - (b) a foolish person
   - (c) a strong person
   - (d) a small child

5. Which of the following might a **typical** American traveling abroad carry?
   - (a) a camera
   - (b) a guide book
   - (c) a bucket
   - (d) a telescope

6. Which of the following might cause a **scarcity** of water?
   - (a) too much demand for it
   - (b) too little rain
   - (c) a flood
   - (d) thirst

7. Which of the following might cause **astonishment?**
   - (a) a summer snowstorm
   - (b) a flying car
   - (c) a talking cat
   - (d) a red apple

8. Which of the following can be **confirmed?**
   - (a) a sigh
   - (b) a result
   - (c) a fact
   - (d) beauty

In Lesson 5 you learned that words sometimes have more than one part and that there are names for these different parts. The part that comes at the beginning of a word is called a prefix. Prefixes change the meanings of words, sometimes turning them into their opposites: *un-* changes *happy* to *unhappy*.

It's time now to look at the part that forms the ending of some words. It's called a suffix. Suffixes have an important job also. For one thing, they change words from one part of speech to another.

Change each of the verbs into a noun by adding the correct suffix and writing the word in the space provided. All of the words are from earlier lessons.

1. alter _____

2. confuse _____

3. exclaim _____

4. intend _____

5. persist _____

6. migrate _____

7. prepare _____

8. locate _____

advantage
astonish
confirm
distant
founder
hamlet
host
misgiving
parch
prospect
scarce
shrewd
sole
torment
typical

Read the passage. Then answer the questions that follow it.

The Forty-Niners

The story was in all the newspapers. It was December of 1848. Television and radio were in the **distant** future; newspapers were the **sole** means of finding out what was going on in the world. And something was going on in California! Millions of people in homes across the United States read about it over the breakfast table. President James Polk had just **confirmed** what until then only a few people knew for certain. Gold had been discovered in California, lots of it. Now everyone knew.

A **typical** worker in the 1840s earned about a dollar a day. Gold sold for twenty dollars an ounce. And in California, gold was lying on the ground and in streambeds, just waiting to be picked up. Not surprisingly, thousands of Americans quit their jobs and headed west. Many left behind their families. If they had **misgivings,** they tried to hide them from their wives and children. The plan was to return as soon as they struck it rich. It was now 1849. Those who joined the **hosts** taking part in the California Gold Rush were called the "forty-niners."

There were no airplanes, no trains, no cars, and no roads to California in 1849. San Francisco was a **hamlet** of less than two thousand people. Many Easterners went there by ship. From New York, they had to sail seventeen thousand miles around the tip of South America. The journey took about six months. Those with families and lots of goods to carry traveled overland by covered wagon. This journey also took about six months. Crossing the Nevada desert was the worst part of the journey. Water was **scarce;** often the travelers had drunk the last drop with days to go before the journey's end. They were easy victims for merchants who set out from San Francisco and traveled east to meet the **parched** travelers. These businessmen brought wagons loaded with barrels of water. The travelers could now get water—for a price. **Tormented** by thirst, they paid a dollar, five dollars, even a hundred dollars for a glass of the precious liquid.

Merchants like these took **advantage** of the law of supply and demand. This law states that something is worth whatever someone is willing to pay for it. Sam Brannan understood this law better than anyone. He was a San Francisco merchant and one of the city's **founders.** The people who had first discovered the gold had tried to keep it quiet. But word leaked out. Soon after Brannan heard the news, he repeated it to crowds of eager listeners. He waved a jar of gold dust as proof. Suddenly, lots of people wanted tools for gold digging. They needed pick axes and shovels. They needed the metal pans used to sift through small rocks, water, and sand. And people could get these tools—again, for a price. Before spreading the good news, Brannan had prepared. He had gone around the area **shrewdly** buying up every pick ax, shovel, and pan he could find. A metal pan Brannan bought for twenty cents he could now sell for fifteen dollars. And even at that price, there was no shortage of takers. In nine weeks, Brannan made thirty-six thousand dollars. He went on to become the richest man in California. He was so rich he even printed his own money!

Over a quarter of a million people had poured into California by the mid-1850s. Many of the new arrivals were drawn to San Francisco. The city grew at an **astonishing** rate. The price of a house went up tenfold in less than a year. For a period of time, the number of people living there doubled every ten days. Most never got rich, and many who did were not able to hold on to their newfound wealth. Sam Brannan died a poor man in 1889; he didn't even leave enough money to pay for his own burial. There were some winners, though. These were the forty-niners who had come not to **prospect** for gold but to work hard at ordinary jobs. These were the ones who built California and made it what it is today: the Golden State.

advantage
astonish
confirm
distant
founder
hamlet
host
misgiving
parch
prospect
scarce
shrewd
sole
torment
typical

▶ **Answer each of the following questions in the form of a sentence. If a question does not contain a vocabulary word from the lesson's word list, use one in your answer. Use each word only once.**

1. By what nickname were the **hosts** of people heading for California known?

   _____

   _____

2. How did some businessmen get rich off the suffering of **parched** travelers?

   _____

   _____

3. Why do you think these businessmen took **advantage** of these travelers?

_____

_____

4. Why did water cost so much?

_____

_____

5. Did most people earn a lot of money in the 1840s?

_____

_____

6. Describe some of the **torments** travelers in the desert suffered.

_____

_____

7. Was San Francisco a big city in the early 1840s?

_____

_____

8. What **misgivings** might some of the people who left their homes in the East have had?

_____

_____

9. Who was Sam Brannan?

_____

_____

10. In what way had Sam Brannan acted **shrewdly** before spreading the news that gold had been discovered?

_____

_____

11. Which well-known person **confirmed** that gold had been found in California?

_____

_____

12. What was the **distance** between New York and California by boat?

_____

_____

13. How might you describe the growth of San Francisco between 1850 and 1855?

_____

_____

14. What are people who try to find gold called?

_____

_____

15. What was the **sole** means of finding out what was going on in California in the days before radio and television?

_____

_____

advantage

astonish

confirm

distant

founder

hamlet

host

misgiving

parch

prospect

scarce

shrewd

sole

torment

typical

FUN & FASCINATING FACTS

Astound (Lesson 4) and **astonish** are synonyms. A third synonym, less common, is *thunderstruck*. It expresses even greater surprise. If you are thunderstruck, you feel as if you have been struck by lightning, thunder's frequent companion. *Astound* and *astonish* are formed from the Latin word *tonere,* meaning "to thunder"!

In Exercise D you learned how suffixes change one part of speech to another; for example, the suffix *-ation* changes the verb *alter* into the noun *alteration.* Another suffix, *-ess,* changes nouns that refer to males into nouns that refer to females. *Lion* becomes *lioness, actor* becomes *actress,* and *host* becomes *hostess.*

Word List

Study the definitions of the words. Then do the exercises that follow.

ail
āl

v. To cause sickness, pain, or trouble.
"What **ails** you?" the doctor asked.

ailment *n.* An illness; a disease.
Measles is a common childhood **ailment.**

ailing *adj.* In poor health.
I have been **ailing** all winter.

banish
ba´nish

v. 1. To force someone out of the country.
When the tsars ruled Russia, lawbreakers were **banished** to Siberia.

2. To get rid of completely.
Joe was such a cheerful person, he **banished** gloom wherever he went.

communicate
kə myoo´ ni kāt

v. To make known; to give or exchange information.
Since I hate to write letters, we **communicate** mostly by telephone.

communication (kə myoo ni kā´ shən) *n.* The exchange of information between people.
The misunderstanding was caused by a lack of **communication** between us.

communicative *adj.* Willing to speak; eager to talk.
When I asked her where she had been, she was not very **communicative,** replying only, "Out."

console
kən sōl´

v. To make less sad; to comfort.
My parents tried to **console** me when my best friend moved away.

consolation (kän sə lā´ shən) *n.* Comfort.
I knew I could always turn to my aunt for **consolation** whenever I was upset.

cower
kou´ ər

v. To shrink from, as if from fear.
When I saw the poor dog **cower,** I knew its master was cruel.

deliberate
di li´ bə rət

adj. Carefully thought out; not hasty.
Although my mother was angry, she spoke in a calm and **deliberate** manner.

v. (di li´ bərāt) To think carefully in order to make up one's mind.
We **deliberated** a long time before deciding to move to Arizona.

© SSI • DO NOT DUPLICATE

depth depth	*n.* Distance from top to bottom or front to back; deepness. The floodwaters reached a **depth** of several feet. **depths** *n. pl.* The innermost part or the deepest part. The treasure chest lay buried in the **depths** of the sea.
desire di zīr´	*v.* To wish for; to want very much. A person who is famished **desires** just one thing—food! *n.* A strong wish. Pizarro's **desire** for gold was so great he ordered the Inca king, Atahualpa, to fill three rooms with it. **desirable** *adj.* Pleasing, agreeable. My new school is in a very **desirable** location.
livelihood līv´ lē hood	*n.* The means of supporting oneself. The storekeepers in Key West depend on tourists for their **livelihood.**
misfortune mis fôr´ chən	*n.* 1. Bad luck; trouble. He had the **misfortune** to break his leg right before the big game. 2. An unlucky event. The 1992 hurricane was Florida's worst **misfortune** in many years.
orphan ôr´ fən	*n.* A child whose parents are dead. Tom Sawyer lived with his Aunt Polly because he was an **orphan.**
precipice pre´ sə pəs	*n.* A very high and steep cliff. We stood watchfully on the edge of the **precipice** and looked down. **precipitous** (pri si´ pə təs) *adj.* 1. Very steep. The Two-Mile Terror ski trail has many **precipitous** slopes. 2. Hasty; abrupt; done without careful thought. Joining the Navy so suddenly was a **precipitous** act.
regain ri gān´	*v.* To get back. By following the doctor's orders, I slowly **regained** my health.
slay slā	*v.* To kill violently. (**slain,** past participle) The scene where Saint George **slays** the dragon comes right at the end of the play.
symptom simp´ təm	*n.* A sign of something. Headaches can be a **symptom** of eyestrain.

Choose two phrases to form a sentence that correctly uses a word from Word List 10. Write each sentence in the space provided.

1. (a) To slay someone is to   (c) send that person away.
   (b) To banish someone is to   (d) tell that person something.

   _____

   _____

2. (a) One's misfortune is   (c) the way one makes a living.
   (b) the way one treats   (d) One's livelihood is
        other people.

   _____

   _____

3. (a) A precipitous drop in price is   (c) A gradual drop in price is
   (b) one that is steep and sudden.   (d) one that is very small.

   _____

   _____

4. (a) To communicate   (c) decide not to take it.
        something is to
   (b) get it back.   (d) To regain something is to

   _____

   _____

5. (a) to be loved.   (c) To be ailing is
   (b) to be ill.   (d) To be deliberate is

   _____

   _____

6. (a) Consolation is   (c) the giving of information.
   (b) Communication is   (d) a series of unlucky events.

   _____

   _____

7. (a) A deliberate change   (c) is one that is agreeable.
   (b) A desirable change   (d) is one that is hardly noticed.

   _____

   _____

8. (a) To slay someone is to   (c) To console someone is to
   (b) comfort that person.   (d) fear that person.

   _____

   _____

9. (a) a large sum of money.   (c) the distance from top to bottom.
   (b) Depth is   (d) Misfortune is

   _____

   _____

10. (a) a close family member.   (c) A symptom is
    (b) a sign of something.   (d) An orphan is

   _____

   _____

ail
banish
communicate
console
cower
deliberate
depth
desire
livelihood
misfortune
orphan
precipice
regain
slay
symptom

Improve each of the following sentences by crossing out the bold phrase and replacing it with a word (or a form of the word) from Word List 10.

1. The judges **gave a great deal of thought and talked among themselves** for a long time before announcing the winner of the science fair.

2. The worst **bad luck** to hit the town was the closing of the shipyard.

3. The King commanded his warriors to **violently kill** his enemies.

4. "You don't look well. What **is the matter with** you?" asked Jorge.

5. He expressed a **strong wish** to spend more time with his children.

6. It took the climbers an hour to descend the **steep cliff that went straight down**.

7. We used to **shrink back in fear** whenever we heard her voice.

8. When Luisa's pet rabbit died, she began writing in her journal every night for **something to give her comfort**.

9. The **children whose parents had died** were all adopted by families in town.

10. If you want this venture to succeed, you must **get rid of** any thoughts of failure.

11. I was moved to the **very deepest parts** of my soul by the sight of the northern lights flashing across the sky.

Circle the letter or letters of each correct answer. A question may have more than one correct answer.

1. Which of the following can have **depth?**
   - (a) a drawer
   - (b) a pond
   - (c) a point
   - (d) a shelf

2. Which of the following might an actor **desire?**
   - (a) perfect teeth
   - (b) applause
   - (c) decayed teeth
   - (d) a good role

3. Which of the following is a way to **communicate?**
   - (a) watching television
   - (b) talking on the phone
   - (c) reading a book
   - (d) writing a letter

4. Which of the following is an **ailment?**
   - (a) measles
   - (b) anger
   - (c) baldness
   - (d) hunger

5. Which of the following might be a person's **livelihood?**
   - (a) attending school
   - (b) mowing lawns
   - (c) washing cars
   - (d) taking out the trash

6. Which of the following might be a **deliberate** act?
   - (a) stumbling
   - (b) building a house
   - (c) writing a report
   - (d) sneezing

7. Which of the following could be **precipitous?**
   - (a) a fall in price
   - (b) an action
   - (c) a cliff
   - (d) a road

8. Which of the following could be **regained?**
   - (a) one's youth
   - (b) one's health
   - (c) the trust of a friend
   - (d) the lead in a race

ail
banish
communicate
console
cower
deliberate
depth
desire
livelihood
misfortune
orphan
precipice
regain
slay
symptom

Turn to the Word List for this lesson and look up *deliberate*. Notice that it has two different pronunciations. When used as an adjective, the last syllable rhymes with *hit*. When used as a verb, the last syllable rhymes with *late*.

Several other words from earlier lessons are also pronounced differently depending on whether they are used as nouns or verbs. There are two syllables in each word pair below, and we stress (say more forcefully) either the first or the second syllable depending on whether the word is used as a verb or a noun. In the pronunciation guide, an accent mark follows the stressed syllable. The word *banish* is pronounced *ba´nish*, with the stress falling on the first syllable: BA-nish.

For each sentence, underline the syllable that is stressed in the word in bold. To the right of each sentence, write whether the word is a verb or a noun.

1. To **project** your voice, you speak to the back of the room. _____

2. A **project** of this size will take years to complete. _____

3. You can get a parking **permit** at the town hall. _____

4. The town does not **permit** overnight parking on Main Street. _____

5. We expect to sign the **contract** at tomorrow's meeting. _____

6. Metals **contract** as they get colder. _____

7. If the pottery is a factory **reject,** we sell it for half price. _____

8. If you **reject** your friend's offer, you might regret it later. _____

9. We **progress** slowly, one small step at a time. _____

10. Tim's latest school report shows he made **progress** in math and science. _____

Tokoyo and the Sea Monster

Folktales are stories passed on from adults to children without ever being written down. Every country has its folktales, and this one comes from Japan. It is the story of a young pearl diver named Tokoyo.

The people of Tokoyo's village made their **livelihood** diving for pearls. They searched for the one oyster in a thousand that contained a precious pearl. Tokoyo was the youngest of the divers. She could stay underwater longer and collect more oysters than anyone. The sea was like a second home to her. She swam easily through its **depths.** She cut oysters from the rocks with her razor-sharp pearling knife.

The other pearl divers were all the family Tokoyo had. Her mother had died when she was a baby. Then, while she was still a child, **misfortune** struck again. Her father had a sense of humor that sometimes got him into trouble. One day he had made a joke about the fact that the emperor was always sick. But making fun of the emperor was a crime. Tokoyo's father was **banished** to the island of Oki, far from the Japanese mainland. To make matters worse, **communication** between Tokoyo and her father was forbidden. Her friends tried to **console** the young girl, but they could not lift her spirits. She felt like an **orphan.** The house that had once been filled with laughter was now filled with sorrow.

Tokoyo's one **desire** was to see her father. On her fifteenth birthday, she left her village and set off for Oki. Soon after landing on the island, Tokoyo saw a group of people standing on the edge of a cliff. With them was a girl about her own age dressed all in white. People explained to Tokoyo that an evil sea god made its home in the waters off the island. This god demanded the life of a young girl once a year. They told Tokoyo that the girl **cowering** before them had been chosen as the sea god's victim. She was about to be thrown into the sea. Then they said that the sea god had also cast a spell on the emperor, causing his many **ailments.** When she heard this, Tokoyo saw a chance to help her father. She begged the people to let her take the girl's place. They began to **deliberate** among themselves while Tokoyo waited anxiously. Finally, to her great relief, they agreed.

ail
banish
communicate
console
cower
deliberate
depth
desire
livelihood
misfortune
orphan
precipice
regain
slay
symptom

Tokoyo walked to the edge of the **precipice.** She took a deep breath and leaped into the water. She swam deeper and deeper. At the bottom of the sea, she found herself face to face with the evil sea god. Tokoyo attacked with her pearling knife, **slaying** him. The spell he had cast on the emperor was broken. In an instant, all the emperor's **symptoms** disappeared. He was delighted to be rid of the doctors who had attended him. When he learned of Tokoyo's brave deed, he promised the young girl whatever she wanted. As a result of Tokoyo's wish, her father **regained** his freedom and was happily reunited with his daughter.

▶ **Answer each of the following questions in the form of a sentence. If a question does not contain a vocabulary word from the lesson's word list, use one in your answer. Use each word only once.**

1. Explain why the story of Tokoyo and the evil sea god has a happy ending.

   _____

   _____

2. Was Tokoyo an **orphan?** Explain your answer.

   _____

3. What does "**misfortune** struck" mean as it is used in the passage?

   _____

   _____

4. Why did the emperor need doctors?

   _____

   _____

5. How does the passage make clear that Tokoyo's friends were kind to her?

   _____

   _____

6. Where did the evil sea god live?

_____

_____

7. Explain why Tokoyo's fight with the sea god was a **deliberate** act.

_____

_____

8. Why didn't Tokoyo's father write to her?

_____

_____

9. Why was Tokoyo's father living on the island of Oki?

_____

_____

10. Why did Tokoyo go to the island of Oki?

_____

_____

11. Why had the girl in white been taken to the **precipice?**

_____

_____

12. How can you tell that the girl in white was afraid?

_____

_____

13. Why did Tokoyo want to take the girl's place?

_____

_____

14. How did the emperor know that the spell had been broken?

_____

_____

ail

banish

communicate

console

cower

deliberate

depth

desire

livelihood

misfortune

orphan

precipice

regain

slay

symptom

15. Why did the people of Tokoyo's village dive for oysters?

_____

_____

FUN & FASCINATING FACTS

- One of the world's oldest languages is Sanskrit. It was spoken in India thousands of years ago and is the special language of the Hindu religion. Very few people speak it today, but some words in European languages are connected to Sanskrit. **Orphan** is one of them. An *orphan* is a child without parents who therefore can be in a weak and helpless state. The word comes from the Sanskrit *arbha,* which means "weak; helpless."

- This lesson includes the word **slay,** which is a homophone of *sleigh.* A *sleigh* is a carriage on runners that travels over snow. *Sleigh* and *slay* are pronounced the same way.

For more practice and games, go to www.WordlyWise3000.com.

Word List	Study the definitions of the words. Then do the exercises that follow.

annual
an´ yoo əl

adj. Happening every year.
Somerville's **annual** town meeting is in March.

n. 1. A plant that lives for one year.
Impatiens is my favorite **annual.**

2. A book that comes out once a year.
I save all my NFL football **annuals.**

artificial
är tə fish´əl

adj. Made by human beings and not by nature.
My aunt Rosa says she can taste the difference between **artificial** sweeteners and real sugar.

blend
blend

v. 1. To come or mix together into one.
Make sure you **blend** the butter and sugar before you add the flour.

2. To go together.
The painter chose colors that **blend** well.

n. A mixture.
Mocha is a **blend** of chocolate and coffee.

bore
bôr

v. 1. To make a round hole in by drilling.
If you **bore** a hole in the wood first, you won't split it when you put in the screw.

2. To tire by being dull and uninteresting.
The yawns of my listeners told me I was beginning to **bore** them.

n. A dull and uninteresting person.
He tells that same joke so often that he is becoming a terrible **bore.**

boring *adj.* Dull and uninteresting.
She sometimes stretches the facts a little, but her stories are never **boring.**

boredom *n.* A state of being bored.
When heads began to nod and eyes to close, you could tell **boredom** had set in.

considerable
kən sid´ ər ə bəl

adj. Great; large.
Although my grandmother's house is a **considerable** distance from town, she walks to the post office there every day.

crude kro͞od	*adj.* 1. Raw; in an unrefined state. Refineries turn **crude** oil into gasoline. 2. Roughly made. Andrea drew me a **crude** map with a crayon on a scrap of paper. 3. Ill-mannered. As we walked back from school, we tried to ignore their **crude** remarks.
evaporate i va´ pə rāt	*v.* 1. To change from water into steam or vapor. The water in the kettle boiled so long that it all **evaporated.** 2. To disappear. By the third day on the mountain, our hopes of being rescued began to **evaporate.**
foliage fō´ lē ij	*n.* The leaves of trees and other plants. The house at the end of the road was completely hidden by **foliage.**
gash gash	*n.* A long, deep cut. When Liza slipped on the rocks, she had to go to the hospital to have the **gash** in her leg stitched up.
hue hyo͞o	*n.* A color; especially a shade of color. The poppies in Monet's paintings stand out because of their vivid reddish-orange **hue.**
increase in krēs´	*v.* To make or become larger; to add to. I'm going to ask my mother to **increase** my allowance on my next birthday. *n.* (in´ krēs) The amount by which something gets larger. A wet spring usually means an **increase** in the number of mosquitoes.
nourish nʉr´ ish	*v.* To feed; to support or make grow. We **nourish** our bodies best by eating a diet of fruits, vegetables, and grains. **nourishment** *n.* Anything that feeds or helps to make grow. When I had the flu, the only **nourishment** I could take was clear chicken broth.
vary ver´ ē	*v.* To make or have a change in. The length of a calendar month **varies** between twenty-eight and thirty-one days. **variation** (ver ē ā´ shən) *n.* A change in form, position, or condition. There isn't much **variation** between the summer and the winter temperatures where my grandfather lives.

vision	*n.* 1. Eyesight.
vi´zhən	If you are lucky enough to have 20/20 **vision,** you'll be able to see well.
	2. Something seen in the mind, especially of the future.
	The founders of the United Nations had a **vision** of a world without hunger or war.
	visual *adj.* Of or used in seeing.
	As a **visual** aid, the speaker projected pictures onto a large screen.
yield	*v.* 1. To give up someone or something; to surrender.
yēld	Congress finally **yielded** to the president's demands and passed the budget.
	2. To produce.
	Twenty gallons of milk will **yield** about one pound of butter.
	n. The amount produced.
	The farmer told us that you can expect a **yield** of about fifty pounds of fruit from each apple tree.

11A ▷ Finding Meanings

Choose two phrases to form a sentence that correctly uses a word from Word List 11. Write each sentence in the space provided.

annual
artificial
blend
bore
considerable
crude
evaporate
foliage
gash
hue
increase
nourish
vary
vision
yield

1. (a) one that is quite large.   (c) An increased amount is
   (b) A considerable amount is   (d) one that is reduced.

_____

_____

2. (a) is not fully developed.   (c) A visual aid is one that
   (b) An artificial aid is one that   (d) helps one to see.

_____

_____

3. (a) A blend is   (c) A bore is
   (b) a long, deep cut.   (d) a dull and uninteresting person.

_____

_____

4. (a) A gash is   (c) something that appears once a year.
   (b) a round hole made by a drill.   (d) An annual is

   _____

   _____

5. (a) To increase is   (c) to grow.
   (b) to be mixed together.   (d) To evaporate is

   _____

   _____

6. (a) Crude rubber is   (c) still in a raw state.
   (b) Artificial rubber is   (d) a mixture of different kinds.

   _____

   _____

7. (a) Colors that blend   (c) quickly fade.
   (b) go well together.   (d) Colors that vary

   _____

   _____

8. (a) A gash is   (c) a careless remark.
   (b) a deep cut.   (d) A hue is

   _____

   _____

9. (a) to give way.   (c) To evaporate is
   (b) To yield is   (d) to melt.

   _____

   _____

10. (a) the wood that comes from it.   (c) its leaves.
    (b) A tree's foliage is   (d) A tree's hue is

   _____

   _____

11. (a) Something that nourishes   (c) does not stay the same.
    (b) Something that varies   (d) keeps getting smaller.

   _____

   _____

Improve each of the following sentences by crossing out the bold phrase and replacing it with a word (or a form of the word) from Word List 11.

1. The **amount produced** from these oil wells is a thousand barrels a day.

2. Basil is one type of **plant that grows for just one season.**

3. Mr. Martinez loves to talk about his new computer, but he can get very **dull and uninteresting.**

4. Spilled gasoline **turns to vapor** and mixes with the air quickly.

5. Manure **provides food for** growing plants.

6. The **roughly made** drawing was the work of a very young child.

7. Julio's favorite sandwich filling is made by **mixing together** peanut butter and honey.

8. These interior paints come in many different **shades of color.**

9. Isabel is a person whose **sense of the future** of the city's parks will be appealing to both young and old.

10. The flowers on the piano look so real that you cannot tell they are **made by human hands.**

annual
artificial
blend
bore
considerable
crude
evaporate
foliage
gash
hue
increase
nourish
vary
vision
yield

Circle the letter or letters of each correct answer. A question may have more than one correct answer.

1. Which of the following might **evaporate?**
   (a) coal
   (b) water
   (c) gasoline
   (d) electricity

2. Which of the following is an **increase?**
   (a) from Maine to Mexico
   (b) from A to Z
   (c) from a scarcity to a lot extra
   (d) from several to many

3. Which of the following is a **considerable** amount?
   (a) ten cents
   (b) a thousand dollars
   (c) fifty tons
   (d) a modest sum

4. Which of the following have **foliage?**
   (a) rose bushes
   (b) apple trees
   (c) mushrooms
   (d) tomatoes

5. Which of the following could cause a **gash?**
   (a) a sharp rock
   (b) a baseball
   (c) a hammer
   (d) an ax

6. Which of the following is a **hue?**
   (a) pink
   (b) yellow
   (c) clear
   (d) dark

7. For which of the following would you need your **vision?**
   (a) making sure your socks match
   (b) observing Thanksgiving
   (c) listening to the radio
   (d) observing the moon

8. Which of the following would a seven-year-old probably find **boring?**
   (a) a visit to a circus
   (b) a ride on a roller coaster
   (c) a speech by a state senator
   (d) a TV discussion of proper diet

Write the antonym of each word on the left on the line next to it. Choose from the words on the right, which are in a different order.

1. increase _____ natural

2. descend _____ lose

3. considerable _____ cramped

4. ancient _____ refined

5. spacious _____ lessen

6. artificial _____ new

7. regain _____ worthless

8. console _____ rise

9. precious _____ slight

10. crude _____ upset

annual
artificial
blend
bore
considerable
crude
evaporate
foliage
gash
hue
increase
nourish
vary
vision
yield

11E Passage

Read the passage. Then answer the questions that follow it.

Maple Sugaring

In the late fall, one of nature's most beautiful sights is the **foliage** of New England's maple trees. The leaves blaze with color. Their **hues** range from bright reds to rich golds.

In the spring, some trees offer more than just a **visual** treat. Early in the season, buckets hang from the sides of sugar maples. The buckets are collecting sap for the **annual** maple sugaring.

How much sap can be collected from a healthy tree? The amount **varies** from twelve to twenty gallons. Amounts in this range **yield** from two to four pounds of maple syrup. This leaves plenty of sap for the tree. The tree needs enough sap to **nourish** itself as it enters a new growing season.

The weather has a great deal to do with how much sap a tree produces. The flow is greatest when the days are sunny and the nights are cold. The flow of sap slows down at night; it **increases** during the day. Maple trees in low, wet areas produce more sap than trees in higher and drier parts. However, the sap from wetter areas contains less sugar.

Native Americans showed the first settlers how to make maple syrup. They made **gashes** in the trees with axes to let the sap run out. However, this could cause **considerable** damage to the tree. Today, tree farmers **bore** a small hole into each tree, about three feet above the ground. This way, they do no harm.

When it seeps from the tree, the syrup is in **crude** form; it needs to be refined before it is ready to use. It is boiled in large kettles until the water **evaporates.** The remaining syrup is passed through filters to clean it. It is then ready to be poured on waffles and pancakes. It can also be made into candy. Maple sugar candy is very popular with visitors to New England.

Maple syrup is produced only in North America. The sugaring season lasts just four to six weeks. Besides New England, several other northern states carry out maple sugaring. The Canadian provinces of Quebec and Ontario also produce maple syrup. Much of the syrup that Americans pour on their pancakes is not real maple syrup, however. It is made from cane sugar syrup with **artificial** maple flavoring added. Sometimes the makers **blend** it with real maple syrup. That way, the label can say "Contains Real Maple Syrup." One hundred percent maple syrup costs more. Still, those who enjoy its taste say there is nothing like the real thing.

▶ **Answer each of the following questions in the form of a sentence. If a question does not contain a vocabulary word from the lesson's word list, use one in your answer. Use each word only once.**

1. What do the words "Contains Real Maple Syrup" on the label tell you?

_____

_____

2. Why do you think **artificial** maple syrup costs less than the real thing?

_____

_____

3. What is another word for the leaves of a tree?

_____

_____

4. In what season do maple trees become a **visual** treat?

_____

_____

5. If you were hiking in New England in the fall, what **hues** might you see?

_____

_____

6. How much sap can be collected from a sugar maple?

_____

_____

7. What is the meaning of **yield** as it is used in the passage?

_____

_____

8. Why do trees produce sap?

_____

_____

9. Why do you think people gathering sap prefer sunny days?

_____

_____

annual
artificial
blend
bore
considerable
crude
evaporate
foliage
gash
hue
increase
nourish
vary
vision
yield

10. Why did the first settlers need axes to get at the sap?

_____

_____

11. Why don't people use this method any more?

_____

_____

12. Explain why you might see small round holes in the trunks of sugar maples.

_____

_____

13. Why don't people use the syrup that collects in the buckets immediately?

_____

_____

14. What happens when sap is boiled?

_____

_____

15. How often does maple sugaring occur?

_____

_____

FUN & FASCINATING FACTS

- Here are two more pairs of homophones. The first is **bore** and *boar;* a *boar* is a male pig. The second is **hue** and *hew;* to *hew* something is to cut it or chop it with an ax.

- **Crude** and *refined* are antonyms. (*Crude* sugar is purified by boiling and filtering; it then becomes *refined* sugar.)

Word List	Study the definitions of the words. Then do the exercises that follow.

ability
ə biˊ lə te

n. Power or knowledge; skill.
Lani's **ability** to do math problems in her head astounded her teacher.

amiable
āˊ mē ə bəl

adj. Friendly; good natured and pleasant.
My uncle's **amiable** manner put my friends at ease right away.

bliss
blis

n. Complete joy or happiness.
My idea of **bliss** is an afternoon on the river with my fishing rod.

blissful *adj.* Very happy; joyful.
The proud parents wore **blissful** smiles as they watched their son graduate.

caress
kə resˊ

v. To touch in a tender or loving way.
Sean **caressed** the baby's forehead gently as it lay sleeping.

n. A tender or loving touch or hug.
The kitten brushing against my cheek felt like a **caress.**

clutch
kluch

v. To grasp or hold tightly to.
Kabir **clutched** his teddy bear as he climbed into the dentist's chair.

n. The part of a machine that connects and disconnects the power from the rest of the machine.
Before changing gears in a standard shift car, first step on the **clutch.**

coax
kōks

v. To persuade or urge in a gentle way.
I **coaxed** my baby sister into holding my hand as we crossed the street.

furious
fyoorˊ ē əs

adj. 1. Very, very angry.
The emperor was **furious** when he realized how the two "tailors" had tricked him.

2. Very fast, strong, or wild.
I was confused by the **furious** activity going on in the kitchen.

fury *n.* 1. Great anger.
Mark's uneasiness turned to **fury** when he learned how completely he had been tricked.

2. Wild and uncontrolled force.
The **fury** of the storm was far greater than had been forecast.

gesture
jes´ chər

n. 1. A movement of the arm or hand.
The president waved his arm in a farewell **gesture** before boarding Air Force One.

2. Something done to show one's feelings.
Asking you to the birthday party was Dolores's **gesture** of friendship.

v. To make a movement of the arm or hand.
The coach **gestured** to the players on the bench to join her on the field.

mope
mōp

v. To be sad and gloomy; to lose interest in the things that usually bring pleasure.
As the long, hot summer days went on and I still had no job, I began to **mope.**

prefer
pri fər´

v. To like better; to choose first.
Which do you **prefer,** chocolate or vanilla?

preference (pre´ fər əns) *n.* That which is preferred.
If you don't have a **preference,** I'll choose the movie.

recover
ri kuv´ ər

v. 1. To get back to a normal state; to get well again.
Patrizia soon **recovered** from the flu.

2. To get back what was lost or stolen.
It cost a hundred dollars to **recover** my car after it was towed.

recovery *n.* 1. A return to a normal state.
Dr. Holberg was surprised at the speed of my **recovery.**

2. The act of getting back what was lost or stolen.
The museum is offering a reward for the **recovery** of the missing painting.

replace
ri plās´

v. 1. To take the place of.
Who will **replace** Mr. Myers when he leaves the school?

2. To put back in place.
When you are through with the encyclopedias, let the librarian **replace** them on the shelves.

replacement *n.* A person or thing that takes the place of another.
If the water pump cannot be repaired, the plumber will order a **replacement** for us.

request
ri kwest´

v. To ask for.
I **requested** a chocolate cake with cherry frosting for my birthday.

n. The thing asked for.
The band leader agreed to play our **request.**

separate	v. To set or keep apart.
se´ pər āt	Whenever the twins start fighting, my mother **separates** them.
	adj. (se´ pər ət) Not together; not joined.
	The twins asked if they could have **separate** bedrooms.
shun	v. To take special pains to avoid; to keep away from.
shun	Leon ceased his bullying when his classmates started to **shun** him.

12A ▷ Finding Meanings

Choose two phrases to form a sentence that correctly uses a word from Word List 12. Write each sentence in the space provided.

1. (a) To shun something
   (b) To recover something
   (c) is to want it very badly.
   (d) is to have nothing to do with it.

_____

_____

2. (a) To be amiable is to be
   (b) very angry.
   (c) talkative.
   (d) To be furious is to be

_____

_____

3. (a) To separate people is to
   (b) make them angry.
   (c) try to persuade them to do something.
   (d) To coax people is to

_____

_____

4. (a) To prefer something is
   (b) to get it back.
   (c) To recover something is
   (d) to get closer to it.

_____

_____

ability
amiable
bliss
caress
clutch
coax
furious
gesture
mope
prefer
recover
replace
request
separate
shun

5. (a) A caress is
   (b) A request is

   (c) a warm and loving touch.
   (d) a warning of possible danger.

   _____

   _____

6. (a) To clutch something is to
   (b) like it better than
       something else.

   (c) To prefer something is to
   (d) let go of it.

   _____

   _____

7. (a) To separate something is to
   (b) ask for it.

   (c) To request something is to
   (d) hold tightly to it.

   _____

   _____

8. (a) A gesture is

   (b) A replacement is

   (c) someone who takes the place of
       another.
   (d) something said as a joke.

   _____

   _____

9. (a) great anger.
   (b) deep sadness.

   (c) Bliss is
   (d) Fury is

   _____

   _____

10. (a) A clutch is
    (b) A gesture is

    (c) a warning not to get any closer.
    (d) a movement of the arm or hand.

    _____

    _____

Improve each of the following sentences by crossing out the bold phrase and replacing it with a word (or a form of the word) from Word List 12.

1. Andrea and Lucia have to be **kept apart** because they giggle so much if they sit together.

2. I **made a movement of my arm** to draw attention to the car I was interested in driving.

3. I had just one **thing I wanted to ask for,** and that was a large glass of cold lemonade.

4. Irina had the chicken pox, but made a quick **return to good health.**

5. Angela **lost interest in the things that usually gave her pleasure** for weeks after Julio moved away.

6. Our old car needs a new **part that connects and disconnects power from the engine.**

7. Around 1900, the automobile began to **take the place of** the horse and buggy.

8. My **having knowledge of how** to speak Spanish was what got me the job in the office.

9. The runners set off at a **very fast** pace.

10. A look of **complete happiness** crossed Mai-ying's face when she heard that she had won the scholarship.

ability
amiable
bliss
caress
clutch
coax
furious
gesture
mope
prefer
recover
replace
request
separate
shun

Circle the letter or letters of each correct answer. A question may have more than one correct answer.

1. Which of the following would an **amiable** person do?
   - (a) avoid other people
   - (b) greet you with a smile
   - (c) get angry easily
   - (d) make friends easily

2. Which of the following might a child **caress?**
   - (a) a baby sister
   - (b) a stuffed animal
   - (c) a pet rabbit
   - (d) a porcupine

3. Which of the following might a person **clutch?**
   - (a) a phone call
   - (b) a telephone
   - (c) a baseball bat
   - (d) a baseball score

4. Which of the following is a friendly **gesture?**
   - (a) sending a get-well card
   - (b) closing your eyes
   - (c) holding out your hand
   - (d) turning your back

5. Which of the following might a person who is **moping** do?
   - (a) suggest having a party
   - (b) not answer when spoken to
   - (c) stay home all day
   - (d) call up old friends

6. Which of the following could be **recovered?**
   - (a) lost time
   - (b) a lost ring
   - (c) your balance
   - (d) your health

7. Which of the following can be **replaced?**
   - (a) a book taken from the shelf
   - (b) a lost screwdriver
   - (c) a friend who dies
   - (d) a pet turtle that dies

8. Who would someone be likely to **shun?**
   - (a) an enemy
   - (b) an untrustworthy person
   - (c) a friend
   - (d) a helpful person

12D Word Study

Sometimes words have such similar meanings that it is easy to confuse them. Read the pairs of sentences. Then choose the word that best fits each sentence.

ask / request

1. When I am lost, I usually _____ someone for directions.

2. The driver will let you get out of the bus at Hanover Street only if you _____ a stop there.

shun / avoid

3. I try to _____ the downtown area at rush hour.

4. The students _____ anyone who acts like a bully.

slay / kill

5. In the legend, the hero set out to _____ the dragon.

6. In the movie, we saw a lion _____ a zebra after bringing it down.

desire / wish

7. Did your _____ come true?

8. Their one _____ was to live in freedom.

bliss / happiness

9. True _____ can often be found by serving others.

10. To be young and in love was sheer _____ .

old / ancient

11. The _____ city of Nineveh was in present-day Iraq.

12. Do you have any _____ clothes you want to give away?

alter / change

13. Do you intend to _____ the date of the meeting?

14. A tailor can _____ that jacket so that it fits better.

ability
amiable
bliss
caress
clutch
coax
furious
gesture
mope
prefer
recover
replace
request
separate
shun

Read the passage. Then answer the questions that follow it.

Communicating with Koko

American Sign Language (ASL) is a form of communication that is as rich and flexible as spoken English. It is used by hundreds of thousands of hearing-impaired people. Each **gesture** of the hand or arm has a particular meaning. In the early 1970s, a most unusual student began learning to communicate through ASL. Her name was Koko and her teacher was Dr. Francine Patterson.

Koko, a gorilla, was born in the San Francisco Zoo. While still a baby, she became ill and had to be **separated** from the other gorillas. She lived in a specially equipped trailer, where Dr. Patterson took care of her. Dr. Patterson is a scientist interested in animal behavior. While nursing Koko back to health, she had another goal as well. Slowly and with great difficulty, she taught the young gorilla to communicate using ASL.

Dr. Patterson made up little games for teaching Koko how to use her hands. She began by working on words for food and drink. She would show Koko an object, say the word, and make the sign. For example, she would sign the word for drink before giving Koko a drink. Koko began to show that she understood Dr. Patterson's gestures after only two weeks. Once she made the association between hand movements and the objects they represented, she quickly began to learn words. By eighteen months, she knew twenty-two signs; by three years and three months, she could make seventy-eight understandable signs. Over a period of six years, she learned over a thousand words. She could even string words together to form simple sentences.

Dr. Patterson also used picture books to teach Koko new words. Koko **preferred** looking at books with pictures of gorillas and cats. So when Dr. Patterson asked Koko what she wanted for her birthday, she wasn't surprised when Koko **requested** a cat. Koko was usually a very **amiable** creature. But when she opened Dr. Patterson's present and saw a stuffed animal, she was **furious.** She threw it away. Dr. Patterson tried to **coax** the unhappy gorilla to play with the toy cat. Her attempts failed. Koko knew the difference between a real cat and a toy one. She **shunned** the stuffed animal completely. She wanted a real cat.

A few weeks later Dr. Patterson gave Koko a little gray kitten. Koko picked up the kitten very carefully and **caressed** it gently. When asked what she was going to call it, she signed "All Ball." Perhaps she gave it this name because it had no tail. Without a tail it looked just like a ball of fur. Koko carried All Ball around on her back. The kitten **clutched** Koko's fur, the way baby gorillas do with their mothers. Koko loved to play games with All Ball; the two became close friends.

One day All Ball was hit by a car and died. For days afterward, Koko **moped**—miserable over the loss of her friend. Koko **recovered** her good spirits when Dr. Patterson gave her another kitten to **replace** All Ball. When Koko got her new pet, she picked it up and held it lovingly. A **blissful** look spread over her face.

With language comes the **ability** to make jokes—and also to lie. Koko learned to do both. One day she broke the sink in the trailer. When Dr. Patterson asked her who had done it, Koko signed the name of the person who had been in the trailer with her. Another time she pointed to a white towel and signed "red." She was corrected several times but refused to admit she had made a mistake. Then she slyly picked a tiny piece of lint off the towel. It was red!

▶ **Answer each of the following questions in the form of a sentence. If a question does not contain a vocabulary word from the lesson's word list, use one in your answer. Use each word only once.**

1. What is the meaning of **gesture** as it is used in the passage?

   _____

   _____

2. Why was Koko living in a trailer?

   _____

   _____

3. Did Koko show a **preference** for a particular kind of book?

   _____

   _____

ability

amiable

bliss

caress

clutch

coax

furious

gesture

mope

prefer

recover

replace

request

separate

shun

4. Why did Dr. Patterson choose a cat to give Koko?

_____

_____

5. What kind of personality did Koko have?

_____

_____

6. What is the meaning of **furious** as it is used in the passage?

_____

_____

7. How did Koko respond to Dr. Patterson's **coaxing?**

_____

_____

8. Why did Koko **shun** the toy cat?

_____

_____

9. How did Koko show that she cherished the real kitten?

_____

10. How did All Ball stay on Koko's back?

_____

11. How could Dr. Patterson tell that Koko was sad when All Ball died?

_____

_____

12. What is the meaning of **replace** as it is used in the passage?

_____

_____

13. How could Dr. Patterson tell that Koko was happy with the second cat?

_____

_____

14. What did learning to communicate allow Koko to do?

_____

_____

15. How would you feel if you felt **blissful?**

_____

_____

_____

FUN & FASCINATING FACTS

- You are likely to **caress** those who are most dear to you. This is not surprising, since the word comes from the Latin *caro,* which means "dear." You might think that the word *care* comes from this same Latin root since we care for those who are dear to us, but it comes from something totally different: the Old English word *cearu.*

- The noun **clutch** has an unusual meaning when it is used as the plural noun *clutches.* To be "in the clutches" of something or somebody is to be in the power of that thing or that person. People who are taken hostage are in the *clutches* of those who have taken them prisoner; criminals spend a lot of time trying to avoid the *clutches* of the law.

ability

amiable

bliss

caress

clutch

coax

furious

gesture

mope

prefer

recover

replace

request

separate

shun

Hidden Message In the boxes provided, write the words from Lessons 9 through 12 that are missing in each of the sentences. The number following each sentence gives the word list from which the missing word is taken. When the exercise is finished, the shaded boxes should spell out an interesting observation from the English writer, philospher, and mathematician Bertrand Russell.

1. Marathon runners cover a _____ of over twenty-six miles. **(9)**

2. The _____ in my leg is healing quickly. **(11)**

3. New York was once a small _____ at the tip of Manhattan. **(9)**

4. Rebecca was in _____ until her lost kitten was found. **(9)**

5. The _____ means of escape was through an underground tunnel. **(9)**

6. I stood on the edge of the _____ and looked down. **(10)**

7. We tried to _____ him for the loss of his pet rabbit. **(10)**

8. This year's _____ meeting will be held in May. **(11)**

9. After a year's hard work, I was able to _____ my place on the team. **(10)**

10. When food is _____ , people can go hungry. **(9)**

11. Buy low and sell high is a _____ way of doing business. **(9)**

12. Being light on her feet is a(n) _____ for a ballerina. **(9)**

13. The magician promised us that her next trick would _____ us. **(9)**

14. We built a _____ shelter from cardboard boxes. **(11)**

15. My wages will _____ from $200 to $250 a week. **(11)**

16. Their calm manner helped _____ our fears. **(10)**

17. My brother has the _____ to become an excellent singer. **(12)**

18. The sun's warmth causes the water to _____ . **(11)**

19. The Senate will _____ the new Secretary of Education. **(9)**

20. A headache could be a _____ of flu. **(10)**

21. My _____ came from buying and selling cars. **(10)**

22. The breeze was gentle as a _____ on their faces. **(12)**

23. We tried to _____ them into staying a little longer. **(12)**

24. David was able to _____ Goliath with a slingshot. **(10)**

25. We hope to make the family gathering a(n) _____ event. **(11)**

26. We stayed in _____ rooms at the hotel. **(12)**

27. Annie Lennox gets thousands of _____ for her autograph. **(12)**

28. The _____ of the water is about ten feet. **(10)**

29. I had the _____ to lose my suitcase when I changed trains. **(10)**

30. Andros and Helen made a _____ effort to help the new students. **(10)**

31. The cause of my _____ puzzled the doctors. **(10)**

32. The trees lose their _____ in the fall. **(11)**

33. The host's _____ manner put us at ease. **(12)**

34. My dad was _____ with me for lying to him. **(12)**

35. Romulus and Remus were said to be the _____ of Rome. **(9)**

36. The rose was of a pale yellow _____ . **(11)**

37. This is a _____ of Brazilian and Kenyan coffees. **(11)**

38. I prefer real flowers to _____ ones. **(11)**

39. What you earn at the print shop will _____ from week to week. **(11)**

40. The doctor said my uncle would _____ very quickly. **(12)**

41. When I have nothing to read on vacations, I sometimes _____ . **(12)**

42. I felt the person next to me _____ my arm. **(12)**

43. The police officer _____ to us to cross the street. **(12)**

44. It would _____ me to listen to the same story again. **(11)**

45. It was _____ to lie on the beach without a care. **(12)**

46. Do you _____ spinach or broccoli? **(12)**

47. A _____ of old classmates showed up for the school reunion. **(9)**

48. You should _____ fatty foods if you want to stay healthy. **(12)**

49. We usually _____ by letter. **(10)**

50. The weather forecast gave little _____ of rain. **(9)**

51. Why does the dog _____ when you approach it? **(10)**

52. You need to _____ the damaged parts. **(12)**

53. This field should _____ two tons of potatoes. **(11)**

54. My greatest _____ was to complete college. **(10)**

55. Raja had no _____ that something might go wrong. **(9)**

56. The cool water felt good on my _____ throat. **(9)**

Lesson **13**

For more practice and games, go to **www.WordlyWise3000.com**.

Word List	Study the definitions of the words. Then do the exercises that follow.

appall
ə pôl´

v. To cause horror, shock, or dismay.
The inspectors were **appalled** by the conditions in the prison factories.

appalling *adj.* Causing shock and horror.
The television report exposed the **appalling** treatment of the farm workers.

dejected
di jэk´ təd

adj. Discouraged; low in spirits.
Jesse felt **dejected** when he couldn't find an apartment with low rent.

depend
di pend´

v. 1. To rely on for support.
Many blind persons **depend** on guide dogs.

2. To be based on.
Whether or not I go to the concert **depends** on what my parents say.

dependable *adj.* Reliable.
If you do a lot of driving, you need a **dependable** car.

dreary
drir´ ē

adj. Sad and gloomy.
I pulled up the shades to let more light into Olga's dark and **dreary** apartment.

fanatic
fə nat´ ik

n. A person whose enthusiasm for a belief is extreme.
Uncle Roger ran the restaurant for years, and he was a **fanatic** about cleanliness in the kitchen.

fanatical *adj.* Carrying an interest or enthusiasm to extremes.
Mr. Gradgrind was a **fanatical** believer in the importance of facts.

impact
im´ pakt

n. 1. The striking of one object by another.
The **impact** of the ball bruised the catcher's arm.

2. Forceful impression.
Martin Luther King, Jr.'s "I Have a Dream" speech had a great **impact** on millions of Americans.

invade
in vād´

v. 1. To enter by force in order to take over.
The German army **invaded** Russia in June, 1941.

2. To intrude; to enter in great numbers.
I am putting a lock on my drawer so my little sister won't be able to **invade** my privacy any more.

invasion *n.* The act of invading.
The gypsy moth **invasion** caused the destruction of many Cape Cod pine trees.

---

isolate
ī´ sə lāt

v. To cut off from others.
As soon as my brother broke out in spots the doctor **isolated** him for a week.

isolation (ī sə lā´ shən) *n.* The condition of being isolated.
The cottage's **isolation** makes it appealing to someone seeking a quiet vacation.

isolated *adj.* Cut off from others.
The lighthouse keeper actually enjoyed her **isolated** life.

---

occupy
ä´ kyōō pī

v. 1. To live in; to take up.
My aunt Bianca's family **occupied** the apartment next to us when I was little.

2. To take over by force.
Protesting students **occupied** the school president's office.

occupation (ä´ kyōō pā´ shən) *n.* 1. A person's job or profession.
Nursing is a perfect **occupation** for my brother since he loves helping people.

2. A filling up of time or space.
The sign in the elevator said that **occupation** by more than twelve people was against the law.

---

reveal
ri vēl´

v. 1. To make known.
If you **reveal** the wish you made, it might not come true.

2. To bring into view; to show.
The curtain rose to **reveal** three men sitting on top of a stone wall.

---

rout
rout

n. A disorganized retreat from an attack; a total defeat.
The battle ended in a **rout** as the enemy soldiers dropped their weapons and ran.

v. To defeat completely.
The U.S. basketball players **routed** their opponents in the 1992 Olympic Games.

suspect sə spekt´	*v.* 1. To think of as probably guilty. The police **suspect** the man who used to live upstairs of breaking into our apartment. 2. To suppose that something is true. I **suspect** that she knows more algebra than she thinks she does. *n.* (sus´pekt) A person believed to be guilty. The **suspect** asked to see a lawyer before being questioned.
temporary tem´pə rer e	*adj.* Lasting or made to last for a short time. The town hall provided a **temporary** place for people to stay.
terror ter´ər	*n.* Great fear. Thunder and lightening always fill my grandmother with **terror.** **terrify** *v.* To fill with terror or great fear. The reports of the crime in the neighborhood **terrified** the residents.
tragic tra´jik	*adj.* Causing great sadness; terrible or dreadful. The entire nation grieved over the **tragic** death of Dr. Martin Luther King, Jr. **tragedy** (tra´jə dē) *n.* 1. An event that causes great pain, suffering, or loss of life. The closing of the shipyard would be a **tragedy** for Charlestown. 2. A play that ends sadly as the hero or heroine loses at the end of a great struggle. Shakespeare wrote some of the world's greatest **tragedies.**

13A ▷ Finding Meanings

Choose two phrases to form a sentence that correctly uses a word from Word List 13. Write each sentence in the space provided.

1. (a) travel through it.   (c) To isolate a place is to
   (b) live in it.   (d) To occupy a place is to

   _____

   _____

2. (a) A dependable person   (c) takes things in stride.
   (b) A dejected person   (d) is in low spirits.

   _____

   _____

3. (a) Impact is
   (b) a forceful impression.
   (c) a desire to do good.
   (d) Terror is

   _____

   _____

4. (a) rely on that person.
   (b) To appall someone is to
   (c) play a joke on that person.
   (d) To depend on someone is to

   _____

   _____

5. (a) To reveal a place is to
   (b) To invade a place is to
   (c) make changes in it.
   (d) enter it to take over.

   _____

   _____

6. (a) well cared for.
   (b) To be fanatic is to be
   (c) cut off from others.
   (d) To be isolated is to be

   _____

   _____

7. (a) To suspect something is to
   (b) bring it into view.
   (c) be afraid of it.
   (d) To reveal something is to

   _____

   _____

8. (a) A temporary condition is one
   (b) that causes great sadness.
   (c) that lasts forever.
   (d) A tragic event is one

   _____

   _____

9. (a) To suspect someone is to
   (b) believe that person is guilty.
   (c) make fun of that person.
   (d) To appall someone is to

   _____

   _____

10. (a) A rout is
    (b) one who has extreme beliefs.
    (c) a path that is traveled.
    (d) A fanatic is

    _____

    _____

Improve each of the following sentences by crossing out the bold phrase and replacing it with a word (or a form of the word) from Word List 13.

1. Whether or not I go on the trip to the mountains will **be based** on the condition of my car.

2. The school building seems **dull and gloomy** during winter vacation.

3. A person with measles should be **kept away from other people.**

4. My job making pizza is **not expected to last for very long,** but I love it.

5. I was **shocked and dismayed** to find out that my neighbors had had no heat in their house for four days.

6. When cockroaches **moved in and took over** our kitchen, my mother called the landlord immediately.

7 The detective waited to question the **persons believed to be guilty of the crime** until their lawyer arrived.

8. There was a look of **great fear** in her eyes as she heard the crash of thunder.

9. The Red Sox **completely defeated** the Yankees by a score of 10 to 0.

10. *Hamlet* is one of Shakespeare's most famous **plays that end sadly as the hero loses at the end of a great struggle.**

appall
dejected
depend
dreary
fanatic
impact
invade
isolate
occupy
reveal
rout
suspect
temporary
terror
tragic

Circle the letter or letters of each correct answer. A question may have more than one correct answer.

1. Which of the following should you be able to **depend** on?
   (a) a close friend
   (b) your parents
   (c) a stranger
   (d) a scoundrel

2. Which of the following could you **reveal?**
   (a) your age
   (b) your date of birth
   (c) your thoughts
   (d) your plans for the future

3. Which final basketball score(s) would be a **rout?**
   (a) 102 to 98
   (b) 68 to 12
   (c) 110 to 108
   (d) 72 to 10

4. Which of the following might be thought **dreary?**
   (a) a blissful afternoon
   (b) a bright hue
   (c) an afternoon spent pulling up weeds
   (d) a person who lacks a sense of humor

5. Which of the following could be **temporary?**
   (a) a death
   (b) a job
   (c) a shelter
   (d) a period without rain

6. Which of the following would have an **impact?**
   (a) the death of a president
   (b) a leaf landing on the ground
   (c) the loss of one's job
   (d) a car hitting a tree

7. Which of the following might be **appalling?**
   (a) an increase in crime
   (b) world hunger
   (c) the condition of homeless people
   (d) the number of people in prison

8. Which of the following is an **occupation?**
   (a) poet
   (b) lawyer
   (c) uncle
   (d) teacher

Here are nine Latin roots and their meanings. Many English words are based on these roots.

tempus	(time)	*amicus*	(friend)	*jacere*	(to throw)
rumpere	(to break)	*annus*	(year)	*centum*	(hundred)
visus	(to see)	*locus*	(place)	*solus*	(alone)

Fill in the blank spaces in each sentence with the correct Latin root and its meaning. Choose from the list of Latin roots.

1. To **isolate** someone is to cut that person off from others. The word comes from the Latin _____, meaning _____.

2. An **abrupt** change is one that breaks with the past and comes without warning. The word comes from the Latin _____, meaning _____.

3. To see properly, you need good **vision.** The word comes from the Latin _____, meaning _____.

4. A **century** is a period of one hundred years. The word comes from the Latin _____, meaning _____.

5. A **temporary** position is not expected to last a long time. The word comes from the Latin _____, meaning _____.

6. To **revise** something is to look it over and make necessary changes. The word comes from the Latin _____, meaning _____.

7. An **amiable** manner is one that is friendly. The word comes from the Latin _____, meaning _____.

8. An **annual** event is one that is held every year. The word comes from the Latin _____, meaning _____.

9. To **locate** a place on a map is to find that place. The word comes from the Latin _____, meaning _____.

10. To **eject** someone is to throw that person out. The word comes from the Latin _____, meaning _____.

appall
dejected
depend
dreary
fanatic
impact
invade
isolate
occupy
reveal
rout
suspect
temporary
terror
tragic

Passage

Read the passage. Then answer the questions that follow it.

Anne Frank's Diary

Anne Frank was eleven years old in 1940 when the armies of Adolf Hitler **invaded** Holland, where she lived with her parents and her older sister. Hitler was the Nazi ruler of Germany. He was a **fanatic** in his ideas, and he hated certain groups of people, especially Jews. He planned to do away with all the Jews in Europe. The Frank family was Jewish. They were frightened and **appalled** when Hitler took over Holland.

In **terror,** Anne's family went into hiding. They moved into a small space hidden behind a bookshelf in Mr. Frank's office. Another family joined them. Altogether, eight people **occupied** the crowded space. They **depended** on brave friends who brought them food and news of the outside world. They hoped their stay would be **temporary,** and every day they longed to hear that Hitler had been defeated. But after two years, they were still in hiding.

From 1942 to 1944, Anne Frank kept a diary. She wrote about the things that happened and their **impact** on her life. Although life in these cramped surroundings was very **dreary,** Anne's diary is always interesting. In it she **reveals** her deepest thoughts and feelings. She complains of the **isolation** they all experienced, and she writes of their hopes of one day leading a normal life. No matter how **dejected** she felt, she always made the effort to keep the diary up-to-date.

Being discovered by the Germans was Anne Frank's greatest fear. Any unusual sound from outside—a slamming door, heavy footsteps, German voices—could be a sign of danger. The little group had the use of a toilet, but they could not flush it during the day. Someone nearby might hear it and **suspect** that people were in hiding there.

World War II ended in 1945. Hitler's armies were **routed** in the East by the Russians and in the West by the Americans and the British. But the war's end came too late for Anne Frank. The Germans had found the family's hiding place the year before. Anne and most of her family were killed.

We would not know of Anne's **tragic** story if not for her diary. She left it behind when she was taken away, but family friends found it and saved it. Anne's father managed to survive the war. When he returned home, his family was gone; only his daughter's diary was left. He published the diary to share her story with the world.

► **Answer each of the following questions in the form of a sentence. If a question does not contain a vocabulary word from the lesson's word list, use one in your answer. Use each word only once.**

1. What part of Anne Frank's story had the greatest **impact** on you?

   _____

   _____

2. What terrible misfortune happened to the people of Holland in 1940?

   _____

   _____

3. Why is Hitler such an **appalling** figure in the world's history?

   _____

   _____

4. What was the main reason for Hitler's actions toward Jews?

   _____

   _____

5. Why did the European Jews fear the Germans?

   _____

   _____

6. What is the meaning of **occupied** as it is used in the passage?

   _____

   _____

7. How did Anne Frank's family and friends get food?

   _____

   _____

8. Why did those in hiding think their stay might be **temporary?**

   _____

   _____

9. What might those in hiding have done to make life less **dreary?**

   _____

   _____

appall
dejected
depend
dreary
fanatic
impact
invade
isolate
occupy
reveal
rout
suspect
temporary
terror
tragic

10. Why do you think readers of her diary feel so close to Anne Frank?

_____

_____

11. Why do you think those in hiding complained of feeling **isolated?**

_____

_____

12. At what times do you think Anne Frank might have been most **dejected?**

_____

_____

13. What made it possible for the Frank group to stay hidden for two years?

_____

_____

14. What happened to Adolf Hitler's armies in 1945?

_____

_____

15. Why is Anne Frank's story such a **tragic** one?

_____

_____

FUN & FASCINATING FACTS

- The word **deject** comes from the Latin roots *de*, meaning "away from," and *jacere*, meaning "to throw." Someone who is *dejected* is thrown, or cast down, in spirit. The word **project** (verb) combines the Latin prefix *pro*, meaning "forward," with *jacere*. To *project* something is to throw it forward. A movie *projector* is a machine that throws an image onto a screen.

Many other words are build from *jacere*, including **reject** ("to throw away"), **inject** ("to force, drive, or throw into something"), and **eject** ("to throw out").

- The word **depend** comes from the Latin roots *de* and *dependēre*, meaning "to hang." Something that is *impending* is "hanging," or about to happen.

Lesson **14**

| Word List | Study the definitions of the words. Then do the exercises that follow. |

afford
ə fôrd´

v. 1. To be able to pay for.
Can you **afford** a new pair of running shoes?

2. To be able to do.
When you're on the soccer team, you can't **afford** to miss a night's sleep.

3. To give; to provide.
Music **affords** me much pleasure.

boast
bōst

v. 1. To talk with too much pride in oneself or in what one owns or has done; to brag.
Ben **boasted** about all the games he had won.

2. To have and to take a proper pride in having.
San Francisco **boasts** one of the finest bridges in the world, the Golden Gate Bridge.

n. An act of boasting.
"It was just a **boast,**" Julio said. "I can't really run five miles."

chord
kôrd

n. Three or more notes of music played together.
Becca played a few **chords** on the guitar.

exceptional
ek sep´ shən əl

adj. Unusually good.
The batik cloth was of **exceptional** quality.

fortunate
fôr´ chə nət

adj. Lucky.
You are **fortunate** to have such kind friends.

fringe
frinj

n. 1. An edge made of short lengths of material such as thread, used to decorate clothes, curtains, etc.
My skirt had a **fringe** down the side.

2. An outside edge.
At the concert, I stood at the **fringe** of the crowd.

humble
hum´ bəl

adj. 1. Plain and simple.
Abraham Lincoln was raised in a **humble** log cabin.

2. Not proud; modest.
In her **humble** speech of thanks, the new mayor said she would need all the help she could get.

v. To bring down to defeat.
Our soccer team **humbled** Newton High with a score of seven goals to one.

---

meadow
me´ dō

n. A field of grass or wildflowers.
In the middle of the **meadow** stood a cow and its calf.

---

melancholy
me´ lən käl ē

adj. Filled with sorrow; very sad.
The movie was so sad it left me in a **melancholy** mood.

n. A state of sadness.
His **melancholy** began to affect my mood and I grew more and more dejected.

---

obstinate
äb´ stə nət

adj. Not willing to give in; stubborn.
You can't persuade him to do anything—he's too **obstinate.**

---

plead
plēd

v. 1. To ask for something that is felt to be very important; to beg.
The family **pleaded** with reporters to leave them alone.

2. To respond to a charge by a court of law.
The prisoner said he wished to **plead** not guilty.

---

plunge
plunj

v. 1. To throw oneself into.
We **plunged** into the pool and swam a few laps.

2. To push or force quickly.
I **plunged** the spade into the earth.

3. To drop sharply.
The price of land near the new dump **plunged** last year.

n. A sudden dive or fall.
My spirits took a **plunge** when I saw the first page of the test.

---

relent
ri lent´

v. To become less strict.
My parents finally **relented** and said I could go to the concert.

submit	v. 1. To give to someone to look over or decide about.
sub mit´	Each student is asked to **submit** a picture for the yearbook.
	2. To give in to someone or something.
	My sister was always telling me what to do, but I refused to **submit** to her.

| trudge | v. To walk slowly and heavily, as though with great effort. |
| truj | We had to **trudge** through deep snow to reach the door. |

14A ▶ Finding Meanings

Choose two phrases to form a sentence that correctly uses a word from Word List 14. Write each sentence in the space provided.

1. (a) Fortunate people   (c) are not vain.
   (b) Humble people   (d) change their minds easily.

_____

_____

2. (a) three or more notes played together.   (c) A plunge is
   (b) an edging of short lengths of material.   (d) A chord is

_____

_____

3. (a) A fortunate person is one   (c) who suffers from poor health.
   (b) who is lucky.   (d) A melancholy person is one

_____

_____

4. (a) A boast is   (c) a grassy field.
   (b) A meadow is   (d) a steep hill.

_____

_____

afford
boast
chord
exceptional
fortunate
fringe
humble
meadow
melancholy
obstinate
plead
plunge
relent
submit
trudge

5. (a) beg for something.   (c) To plead is to
   (b) deny something.   (d) To submit is to

   _____

   _____

6. (a) To boast a fine sports stadium   (c) is to take good care of it.
   (b) To afford a fine sports stadium (d) is to take pride in it.

   _____

   _____

7. (a) An exceptional student is   (c) is very lucky.
       one who
   (b) An obstinate student is   (d) has great ability.
       one who

   _____

   _____

8. (a) a sharp drop.   (c) A plunge is
   (b) a change of mind.   (d) A fringe is

   _____

   _____

9. (a) give it to someone for   (c) To submit something is to
       approval.
   (b) To afford something is to   (d) be ashamed of it.

   _____

   _____

10. (a) Obstinate people   (c) are unable to make up their minds.
    (b) Melancholy people   (d) are unwilling to change their minds.

   _____

   _____

Improve each of the following sentences by crossing out the bold phrase and replacing it with a word (or a form of the word) from Word List 14.

1. Raoul had no choice but to **give in** to his parents' rules.

2. After you **say, when asked by the judge, that you are** not guilty, the trial will begin.

3. Our first apartment was **plain and simple,** but we loved it.

4. It was Aunt Oona's **proud claim** that she could run two miles in twelve minutes.

5. At first Mom said we couldn't ride our bikes to the movies, but after thinking it over, she **changed her mind and said that we could.**

6. Neema and Bill **walked slowly and with much effort** up the steep path to the top of Corey Hill.

7. The crowd gasped as the Olympic swimmer **dived suddenly** into the pool.

8. I prefer the tan lampshade with the **edge of short lengths of thread sewn on for decoration.**

9. We were all wondering how Alisa could **spare the money for** all those new clothes.

10. The second movement of Brahms' Fourth Symphony fills me with **feelings of great sadness.**

afford
boast
chord
exceptional
fortunate
fringe
humble
meadow
melancholy
obstinate
plead
plunge
relent
submit
trudge

Circle the letter or letters of each correct answer. A question may have more than one correct answer.

1. Which of the following might a person **boast** about?
   (a) making a mistake   (c) winning
   (b) losing   (d) failing

2. Which of the following might make a person feel **fortunate?**
   (a) having good health   (c) living in a free country
   (b) having kind parents   (d) getting free tickets to the circus

3. Which of the following might have a **fringe?**
   (a) a crowd   (c) a blanket
   (b) a lake   (d) a story

4. Which of the following might be too much for most people to **afford?**
   (a) to go on a trip around the world   (c) to miss a meal
   (b) to spare some time   (d) to buy a sports car

5. Which of the following can be **humble?**
   (a) a person   (c) a speech
   (b) a cottage   (d) a palace

6. Which of the following might you find in a **meadow?**
   (a) cows   (c) wildflowers
   (b) picnickers   (d) skyscrapers

7. Which of the following might a person **plead** for?
   (a) more help   (c) mercy
   (b) more money   (d) misfortune

8. Which of the following can **plunge?**
   (a) the temperature   (c) a rock
   (b) the price of a house   (d) the age of a house

The suffix *-able* changes a verb into an adjective. Change each verb into an adjective by adding this suffix to the word. Note that in words that end with *y* preceded by a consonant, you must change the *y* to *i* before adding the suffix. (*envy, enviable*)

1. depend   _____

2. vary   _____

3. remark   _____

4. prefer   _____

5. afford   _____

6. rely   _____

The suffix *-ment* changes a verb to a noun. Change each verb into a noun by adding this suffix to the word.

7. entertain   _____

8. replace   _____

9. nourish   _____

10. equip   _____

11. achieve   _____

12. resent   _____

afford
boast
chord
exceptional
fortunate
fringe
humble
meadow
melancholy
obstinate
plead
plunge
relent
submit
trudge

Read the passage. Then answer the questions that follow it.

How Water Lilies Began

This is a folktale from Wales, a small country west of England. It tells how water lilies came to grow in a lake in the Welsh mountains. It was all because of Huw, a farmer's son. Huw loved to play the harp and never went to school. He lived with his mother in a **humble** cottage by the side of a mountain. Every morning, he drove his mother's black and white cows up the mountain. There they spent the day in a **meadow** by the side of the lake.

One day, Huw took his harp and played a few **chords** as he watched over the herd. To his astonishment, six silver cows rose out of the water. They were drawn by the music. Their coats gleamed in the sunlight as they gathered around Huw and listened to him play. They stayed with the herd all day. In the evening, they followed the rest of the cows back to the farm that evening. Huw's mother felt very **fortunate** to have such fine new cows. She **boasted** to her neighbors that they gave twice as much milk as the black and white ones. And, she added, the milk was of **exceptional** quality.

All went well until one of the silver cows stopped giving milk. After waiting a few days, Huw's mother went to the butcher. She told him to come the next day and take the cow away. Huw **pleaded** with his mother to spare the animal, but she wouldn't **relent.** She told him that they couldn't **afford** to have even one cow eating grass and giving nothing in return. The boy knew how **obstinate** his mother could be once her mind was made up. He argued with her for as long as he dared. But when his mother told him to be quiet, he had no choice but to **submit** to her will.

The next morning, as he **trudged** up the mountain, Huw could think of nothing but the beautiful silver cow that was going to be sold. The music he played on his harp that day became more and more **melancholy.** At last, his eyes filled with tears, and he could play no more. He stood up and threw his harp into the lake. At once a strange thing happened. The six silver cows ran to the edge of the lake and **plunged** in. They were never seen again.

Soon masses of silver water lilies began to grow. They grew all along the **fringes** of the lake where the silver cows had jumped in. They still grow there today. Huw's mother died long ago, and Huw is now an old man. If you should meet him and tell him you don't believe this story, he will be happy to take you up the mountain and show you the beautiful silver water lilies.

▶ **Answer each of the following questions in the form of a sentence. If a question does not contain a vocabulary word from the lesson's word list, use one in your answer. Use each word only once.**

1. Why might it be easy to pick the water lilies that grew in the lake?

_____

_____

2. How did the music Huw played match his mood?

_____

_____

3. What is the meaning of **afford** as it is used in the passage?

_____

_____

4. How can you tell that Huw's family was not wealthy?

_____

_____

5. How can you tell from the passage that Huw's mother was not a shy person?

_____

_____

6. Where did Huw and the cows go every day?

_____

_____

7. What did the silver cows seem to be responding to?

_____

_____

8. Why was milk from the silver cows worth more than milk from the other cows?

_____

_____

afford
boast
chord
exceptional
fortunate
fringe
humble
meadow
melancholy
obstinate
plead
plunge
relent
submit
trudge

9. Why did Huw's mother feel **fortunate** to have the silver cows?

_____

_____

10. How can you tell from the passage that Huw was unwilling to defy his mother?

_____

_____

11. What did Huw do when his mother said the butcher would take the cow?

_____

_____

12. Did Huw's mother agree to do what he asked?

_____

_____

13. What does the word **trudged** suggest about Huw's feelings as he went up the mountain?

_____

_____

14. Why was it a waste of time for Huw to argue with his mother?

_____

_____

15. What was the last glimpse that Huw had of the silver cows?

_____

_____

- **Chord** has another meaning in addition to the one given. In geometry, a *chord* is a straight line joining any two points on a circle.

  Chord and *cord* are homophones. *Cord* is thick string or twine. It is also a unit of measurement; a *cord* of firewood is a stack that measures eight feet by four feet by four feet.

- In the Middle Ages, over five hundred years ago, people believed that the human body contained four different kinds of fluids, called *humors*. The four humors were blood, phlegm, yellow bile, and black bile. When these were in balance, a person was said to be in good humor; when they were out of balance, a person's mood was affected. Too much blood made a person *sanguine*, or cheerful (the Latin word for blood is *sanguis*). Too much phlegm made a person *phlegmatic*, or slow to respond. Too much yellow bile, called *choler*, made a person *choleric*, or angry. Too much black bile, called *melan choler*, made a person **melancholy**, or unhappy.

For more practice and games, go to www.WordlyWise3000.com.

Word List	Study the definitions of the words. Then do the exercises that follow.

apparent
ə par´ ənt

adj. 1. Clear.
It's **apparent** that no one's home.

2. Seeming or appearing to be.
The **apparent** cause of increase in the price of lettuce was the spring freeze.

ban
ban

v. To forbid, especially by passing a law or making a rule.
The hospital **bans** children from visiting patients.

n. A law or rule that forbids something.
There is a **ban** on wearing hats in class.

concentrate
kän´ sən trāt

v. 1. To focus all one's thoughts or efforts on.
It's hard for me to **concentrate** on homework when I hear the kids outside.

2. To bring or come together in one place.
Factories were **concentrated** along the east side of the Harlem River.

concentration (kän sən trā shən) *n.* Giving total attention to something.
Don't sing! It ruins my **concentration.**

concentrated *adj.* Of increased strength or thickness.
For breakfast, mix one part of **concentrated** orange juice to three parts water.

concern
kən sʉrn´

v. 1. To be about; to interest.
Homelessness is a subject that should **concern** everyone.

2. To trouble or worry.
My parents are **concerned** about my brother's health.

n. 1. Something that involves a person or people.
Health care is a big **concern** for most people.

2. A business organization.
After college she got a job with a banking **concern.**

consider
kən si´ dər

v. 1. To think about carefully.
Since my teaching job is a temporary one, it's time to **consider** what I should do next.

2. To take into account.
Please **consider** my feelings when you comment on the story I wrote.

3. To believe.
I may only be seventeen, but I **consider** myself an adult.

contrast kən trast´	*v.* 1. To compare in order to show the differences. Before deciding on the design for the new gym, we are going to **contrast** the two suggested plans.
	2. To show differences when compared. His actions **contrast** greatly with his words.
	n. (kän´ trast) A difference. Our new apartment is a welcome **contrast** to our old one.
fragile fra´ jəl	*adj.* Easily broken or damaged. This antique chair is so **fragile** that it would break if anyone sat on it.
menace me´ nəs	*n.* Something that is likely to do harm or is regarded as dangerous. Icebergs are a **menace** to ships in the North Atlantic.
	v. To be a danger to; to put at risk. The approaching hurricane **menaces** the entire South Carolina coast.
pounce pouns	*v.* To swoop down on and seize. The cat **pounced** on the mouse as soon as it ventured from its hole.
prompt prämpt	*adj.* Quick; without too much time passing. I sent a **prompt** reply to Ahmed's letter.
	v. To cause to act. Seeing ants all over the counter **prompted** me to spend the afternoon cleaning the kitchen.
recent rē´ sənt	*adj.* Of a time just before the present. The **recent** outbreak of measles resulted in the temporary closing of our school.
symbol sim´ bəl	*n.* Something that stands for something else. The dove is a **symbol** of peace.
talon ta´ lən	*n.* The claw of a bird, usually one that kills animals for food. The hawk clutched its victim firmly in its **talons.**
trophy trō´ fē	*n.* Something, as a prize or award, given to show success in an activity. The Heisman **trophy** is a top football honor.
widespread wīd´ spred´	*adj.* 1. Spread or stretched out over a large area. The **widespread** wings of the condor can reach ten feet from tip to tip.
	2. Happening or found over a large area. There was **widespread** frost last night.

Choose two phrases to form a sentence that correctly uses a word from Word List 15. Write each sentence in the space provided.

1. (a) total attention.　　(c) Concern is
   (b) a lack of interest.　　(d) Concentration is

   _____

   _____

2. (a) An apparent winner is　　(c) A recent winner is
   (b) one who always wins.　　(d) one who seems to have won.

   _____

   _____

3. (a) A concern is　　(c) a business organization.
   (b) A symbol is　　(d) something that is likely to do harm.

   _____

   _____

4. (a) To concentrate things is to　　(c) To pounce is to
   (b) become scarce.　　(d) bring them together in one place.

   _____

   _____

5. (a) took place a short time ago.　　(c) A widespread storm is one that
   (b) A recent storm is one that　　(d) lasted for just a short time.

   _____

   _____

6. (a) A contrast is　　(c) a rule that forbids something.
   (b) an unintended result.　　(d) A ban is

   _____

   _____

7. (a) To prompt something is　　(c) to be a danger to it.
   (b) To menace something is　　(d) to allow it to happen.

   _____

   _____

8. (a) to show how they differ. (c) To consider two things is
   (b) To contrast two things is (d) to prefer one over the other.

   _____

   _____

9. (a) found all over. (c) Something that is widespread is
   (b) broken into pieces. (d) Something that is fragile is

   _____

   _____

10. (a) To prompt something is to (c) To consider something is to
    (b) take it into account. (d) forbid it.

    _____

    _____

11. (a) A trophy is (c) something that stands for
                         something else.

    (b) A symbol is (d) an animal's claw.

    _____

    _____

afford
boast
chord
exceptional
fortunate
fringe
humble
meadow
melancholy
obstinate
plead
plunge
relent
submit
trudge

Improve each of the following sentences by crossing out the bold phrase and replacing it with a word (or a form of the word) from Word List 15.

1. My grandmother's teacups are too **easily broken** to use every day.

2. The kitten **leaped through the air and landed** on the ball of yarn.

3. What **caused** you to embrace the idea of becoming a writer?

4. The eagle's **sharp, curved claws** grasped the fish and lifted it out of the water.

5. Her golfing **award for victory** was the thing she took great pride in.

6. This chapter in the history book **points out the differences between** school life today with that of a century ago.

7. Please **keep your mind only** on your driving, and forget about looking at the scenery.

8. Have you **given any thought to** trading in your old car for a new one?

9. My grandmother's future is a subject that **is of great interest to** my parents.

Circle the letter or letters of each correct answer. A question may have more than one correct answer.

1. Which of the following is a **recent** event?
   (a) this morning's breakfast
   (b) your grandparents' wedding
   (c) last night's supper
   (d) your first day of kindergarten

2. Which of the following is **fragile?**
   (a) a baseball bat
   (b) a glass ornament
   (c) a gold ring
   (d) a tree limb

3. Which of the following might cause **concern?**
   (a) a toothache
   (b) rising prices
   (c) a hurricane warning
   (d) a furious customer

4. Which of the following could be a **menace** to drivers?
   (a) icy roads
   (b) thick fog
   (c) speed limits
   (d) seat belts

5. Which of the following might **pounce** on another animal?
   (a) an elephant
   (b) an eagle
   (c) a tiger
   (d) a mouse

6. Which of the following is a **symbol** of the United States?
   (a) the stars and stripes
   (b) the Statue of Liberty
   (c) the bald eagle
   (d) the Liberty Bell

7. For which of the following might you be given a **trophy?**
   (a) taking care of a little sister
   (b) winning a tennis match
   (c) catching the biggest fish
   (d) catching a cold

8. Which of the following might do **widespread** damage?
   (a) a flood
   (b) a hurricane
   (c) a leaky roof
   (d) an earthquake

afford

boast

chord

exceptional

fortunate

fringe

humble

meadow

melancholy

obstinate

plead

plunge

relent

submit

trudge

The prefix *con-* or *com-* means "with" or "together."

Fill in the first set of blanks with the correct form of the prefix *con-* or *com-* for each word. Fill in the second set with *together* or *with* to complete the meaning. All except the last two words are from this or previous lessons.

1. _____trast   to compare one thing _____ another

2. _____centrate   to bring or come _____ in one place

3. _____municate   to be in touch _____

4. _____plete   _____ nothing missing

5. _____cern   to have to do _____

6. _____fuse   to mix one thing up _____ another

7. _____sider   to think over _____ care

8. _____tract   to draw closer _____

9. _____plain   to find fault _____

10. _____nect   to join one thing _____ another

15E ▶ Passage

Read the passage. Then answer the questions that follow it.

The Fall and Rise of the Bald Eagle

For over two hundred years, the bald eagle has been the **symbol** of America. The likeness of this powerful bird is found on our coins and on the Great Seal of the United States. Two hundred years ago, bald eagles were found throughout North America. By the 1970s, however, there were very few left outside of Alaska. The only creatures that **menace** the bald eagle are human beings. Why were there so few of these birds left? What are they like?

The bald eagle is a large, strong bird that is not really bald. It gets its name from its white-feathered head. The bird's head **contrasts** sharply with the rest of its brown-feathered body. When it flies, it looks as if it is a master of the air. The bald eagle is well equipped to live by hunting; it has keen vision, great **talons,** and a large, strongly hooked beak. Small animals and fish form the greater part of its diet. Sometimes it will **pounce** on a small lamb or piglet. Because of this, ranchers and farmers waged war on bald eagles. For hundreds of years they killed the birds in large numbers. In addition, hunters shot them in order to have them stuffed as **trophies.**

In the 1950s, it became **apparent** that there was a sharp drop in the number of bald eagles. The reason for this was soon discovered. The eagles' eggs were **fragile.** When they broke, the chicks inside died. The cause of the thin shells remained unknown for a number of years. Finally, the mystery was solved by a scientist named Rachel Carson.

Rachel Carson was **concerned** about the use of pesticides. Pesticides are chemicals used to kill insects that damage crops. In 1962, she wrote a book called *Silent Spring*. Her book showed how some chemicals were harming the nation's wildlife. It also explained why the eagle shells were thin: the cause was DDT. This pesticide had been in **widespread** use in the United States for over ten years. DDT had become **concentrated** in lakes and streams. Once it was in the water, it poisoned fish. Bald eagles ate fish that contained DDT. This caused them to lay eggs with thin shells that broke easily.

Rachel Carson hoped that Congress would act **promptly** to end the use of DDT and save the national bird. But it was not until 1973 that Congress passed a law **banning** the use of DDT. In the same year, it also passed a law

afford
boast
chord
exceptional
fortunate
fringe
humble
meadow
melancholy
obstinate
plead
plunge
relent
submit
trudge

that made it a crime to harm certain birds and animals that were **considered** to be in danger. The bald eagle was among them.

Gradually, the bald eagle's numbers began rising. A **recent** count revealed that there were about ten thousand pairs of bald eagles in the United States. In 2007, this grand bird was removed from the national list of animals in danger of dying out. Laws continue to protect the bald eagle, however. It is still illegal to harm bald eagles and their eggs.

▶ **Answer each of the following questions in the form of a sentence. If a question does not contain a vocabulary word from the lesson's word list, use one in your answer. Use each word only once.**

1. When would a farmer be most likely to kill a bald eagle?

_____

_____

2. When did we find out that the bald eagle was in danger of dying out?

_____

_____

3. What was the reason for the drop in the number of bald eagles?

_____

_____

4. Explain why this story of the bald eagle has a happy ending.

_____

_____

5. Why did the bald eagle have good reason to fear human beings?

_____

_____

6. How does the bald eagle capture its food?

_____

_____

7. How did Rachel Carson show her **concern** about what was happening to the nation's wildlife?

_____

_____

8. What happened to DDT after it had been sprayed on crops?

_____

_____

9. Where was DDT used?

_____

_____

10. What did some hunters do with the bald eagles they shot?

_____

_____

11. What is the meaning of **considered** as it is used in the passage?

_____

_____

12. Why was it important for Congress to act **promptly?**

_____

_____

13. What did Congress finally do?

_____

_____

14. How did the bald eagle get its name?

_____

_____

15. Why does a picture of the bald eagle appear on the Great Seal of the United States?

_____

_____

afford
boast
chord
exceptional
fortunate
fringe
humble
meadow
melancholy
obstinate
plead
plunge
relent
submit
trudge

FUN & FASCINATING FACTS

When the Apollo astronauts returned to Earth, they brought back *fragments* of rocks from the moon. The word means "parts that are broken off," and comes from the Latin *fractus,* which means "broken." Several other English words are formed from this same Latin root. If you break a bone, you have a *fracture.* If you break down the number one into smaller parts, such as halves or quarters, you get *fractions.* Finally, something that is **fragile** is easily broken.

When a stage actor forgets the next line, a person off to the side may **prompt** him or her by saying it aloud. The *prompter* must say the line loud enough for the actor to hear but not so loud that the audience hears. If the audience does hear the prompter, the play usually gets an unintended laugh.

A *cymbal* is a musical instrument; it is one of a pair of brass plates that are struck together to make a ringing sound. This word and **symbol** are homophones, words that sound alike but have different meanings and spellings.

For more practice and games, go to **www.WordlyWise3000.com**.

Word List	Study the definitions of the words. Then do the exercises that follow.

apt
apt

adj. 1. Well-suited; fitting; appropriate.
"The Stilt" was an **apt** nickname for seven-foot-one-inch basketball star Wilt Chamberlain.

2. Likely or almost certain.
I am **apt** to do better on Spanish tests if I make vocabulary cards to study.

blossom
blä´səm

n. A flower.
The white orange **blossom** stands out against the dark-green foliage.

v. 1. To come into bloom.
Dogwood trees **blossom** in May.

2. To develop.
After two years of playing bit parts, she **blossomed** into a star of the Broadway stage.

bough
bou

n. A large branch or limb of a tree.
The **boughs** of the apple tree were heavy with fruit.

content
kən tent´

adj. Happy with what one has; satisfied.
Give me a good book and a comfortable armchair and I am **content.**

contentment *n.* A state of being satisfied and at peace.
After a delicious dinner and a hot bath, I relaxed in total **contentment.**

detest
di test´

v. To dislike strongly; to hate.
Many Germans **detested** Hitler, but were afraid to speak out.

detestable *adj.* Causing or deserving strong dislike.
His racist views are **detestable.**

dusk
dusk

n. The time at the end of the day just before dark.
The streetlights go on at **dusk.**

extinguish
ek stin´gwish

v. To put out, as a fire or a light.
The sign at the campsite said, "Before leaving, make sure you **extinguish** your campfire."

familiar	*adj.* 1. Often seen or experienced; known.
fa mil´ yər	I was happy to see a **familiar** face in the crowd.
	2. Having a good knowledge of.
	Dan read about it in the newspaper and is **familiar** with the case.

| **obtain** | *v.* To gain or get by making an effort. |
| əb tān´ | We were lucky to **obtain** tickets for the jazz concert because they sold out very quickly. |

| **orchard** | *n.* A place where fruit trees grow. |
| ôr´ chərd | Every fall my brother and I go to an **orchard** where you can pick your own apples. |

practice	*v.* 1. To say or do over and over in order to get better at something.
prak´ tis	If you **practice** Spanish every day, you should be able to get along when you go to Mexico.
	2. To do; carry on, perform.
	He was raised from an early age to **practice** politeness.
	3. To work at as a profession.
	Aunt Marianna is licensed to **practice** law in both California and Nevada.
	n. 1. A repeated action or usual way of doing something.
	It's my mother's **practice** to swim thirty laps every morning.
	2. The work of a profession.
	The **practice** of medicine has recently undergone many changes.

prune	*v.* To cut off branches.
proon	We had to **prune** the shrubs so we could see out of the window.
	n. A dried plum.
	Elijah usually soaks the **prunes** overnight and serves them for breakfast.

stout	*adj.* 1. Heavily built; thickset.
stout	He used to be thin, but he grew **stout** as he got older.
	2. Strong; not easily bent or broken.
	The roof of the barn was supported by six **stout** posts.

| **threadbare** | *adj.* Shabby and worn-out. |
| thred´ ber | The **threadbare** blankets on the bed failed to keep us warm during the night. |

wander	*v.* 1. To go from place to place with no plan or purpose in mind.
wän´dər	We **wandered** around downtown, waiting for the post office to open.
	2. To slip easily off the subject; to fail to work in a normal way.
	Luis tried to concentrate on his math homework, but his mind began to **wander**.

16A ▶ **Finding Meanings**

Choose two phrases to form a sentence that correctly uses a word from Word List 16. Write each sentence in the space provided.

1. (a) A blossom is
   (b) A practice is
   (c) the work of a profession.
   (d) something that is done right the first time.

_____

_____

2. (a) A familiar person is one who is
   (b) A stout person is one who is
   (c) a close relative.
   (d) heavily built.

_____

_____

3. (a) To extinguish a light is to
   (b) To obtain a light is to
   (c) put it out.
   (d) put a shade over it.

_____

_____

4. (a) To prune is to
   (b) travel aimlessly.
   (c) gather fruit.
   (d) To wander is to

_____

_____

5. (a) whatever is inside something.
   (b) the approach of darkness.
   (c) Contentment is
   (d) Dusk is

_____

_____

apt
blossom
bough
content
detest
dusk
extinguish
familiar
obtain
orchard
practice
prune
stout
threadbare
wander

6. (a) An orchard is
   (b) A blossom is

   (c) a flower.
   (d) a piece of fruit.

   _____

   _____

7. (a) is found after a search.
   (b) Something that is apt

   (c) Something that is detestable
   (d) deserves hate.

   _____

   _____

8. (a) get rid of it.
   (b) keep doing it.

   (c) To practice something is to
   (d) To obtain something is to

   _____

   _____

9. (a) a type of dried fruit.
   (b) a fruit-bearing tree.

   (c) A bough is
   (d) A prune is

   _____

   _____

Improve each of the following sentences by crossing out the bold phrase and replacing it with a word (or a form of the word) from Word List 16.

1. I **strongly dislike** your taste in music.

2. As I crawled along the **branch of the tree,** it began to bend under my weight.

3. If I raise my grade to a B+, I will be **very satisfied.**

4. After an hour of that boring movie, my mind began to **fail to work in a normal way.**

5. My cousin's farm includes a large **piece of land on which fruit trees are growing.**

6. My favorite blue sweater is **getting shabby and worn out,** but I refuse to throw it away.

7. My piano teacher said that if I keep **playing that part over and over again,** I'll have the whole piece memorized.

8. Beginning skiers are **very likely** to fall many times while they are learning.

9. Gina is going to **get hold of** the equipment we need for the camping trip.

10. Your face is **known to me,** but I can't remember your name.

11. When do the rose bushes start to **have flowers growing on them?**

apt
blossom
bough
content
detest
dusk
extinguish
familiar
obtain
orchard
practice
prune
stout
threadbare
wander

Circle the letter or letters of each correct answer. A question may have more than one correct answer.

1. Which of the following might be **stout?**
   (a) a person
   (b) a rope
   (c) a walking stick
   (d) a cobweb

2. Which of the following would grow in an **orchard?**
   (a) pears
   (b) a chord
   (c) potatoes
   (d) tomatoes

3. Which of the following happens at **dusk?**
   (a) the stars begin to appear
   (b) it gets darker
   (c) the sun rises
   (d) it gets cloudy

4. Which of the following can a person **obtain?**
   (a) a car roof rack
   (b) a car trip
   (c) a phone number
   (d) a phone call

5. Which of the following can be **pruned?**
   (a) trees
   (b) leaves
   (c) flowers
   (d) branches

6. Which of the following might bring a person **contentment?**
   (a) being with family
   (b) getting together with friends
   (c) feeling concerned about one's health
   (d) missing an important date

7. Which of the following are **familiar** sights in the city?
   (a) buses
   (b) taxicabs
   (c) shoppers
   (d) police cars

8. Which of the following might **wander?**
   (a) a train
   (b) a lost child
   (c) a person going for a long walk
   (d) a person setting off for work

Write the synonym of each word on the left on the line next to it. Choose from the words on the right, which are in a different order.

1. prompt _____ danger

2. ban _____ sad

3. detest _____ quick

4. plead _____ satisfied

5. threadbare _____ forbid

6. obstinate _____ get

7. fortunate _____ modest

8. obtain _____ hate

9. menace _____ lucky

10. content _____ stubborn

11. humble _____ beg

12. melancholy _____ shabby

apt
blossom
bough
content
detest
dusk
extinguish
familiar
obtain
orchard
practice
prune
stout
threadbare
wander

Read the passage. Then answer the questions that follow it.

The Story of Johnny Appleseed

In the late 1700s, most Americans had never tasted an apple. That's because very few apple trees grew outside of New England. A man named John Chapman did more than anyone else to change that. He enjoyed sinking his teeth into a sweet, juicy apple and wanted to share his enjoyment with others. When he traveled, it was his **practice** to take a bag of apple seeds with him. For forty years, Chapman **wandered** through Ohio, Indiana, and western Pennsylvania. As he went along, he planted apples trees.

Chapman **obtained** the seeds from New England cider mills after the apples had been pressed for cider. Over the years, apple **orchards** began growing in many of the places he had visited. From time to time, he returned to them. He would **prune** the trees and make sure they stayed healthy.

This unusual man was born in Leominster, Massachusetts. He began his travels in 1797, when he was in his early twenties. When he needed money, he knew how to get it. Just down the road, someone would give him work and pay him a dollar or two. Chapman spent most days on the road. In his hand was a **stout** walking stick cut from an apple tree. On his head was a tall, black hat. At **dusk,** he looked for a place to spend the night. If there was no house with a room to offer him nearby, he was **content** to sleep under the stars. He had few needs, and it didn't bother him that his clothes were **threadbare.**

John Chapman **detested** killing of any kind. For that reason, he refused to eat meat. Once he even **extinguished** a campfire because mosquitoes were flying into the flames and dying. He had no fear of wild animals either. The animals, in turn, seemed to sense that he would do them no harm. In one of the many stories told about Chapman, he spent the night in the company of a friendly bear.

When he returned to places he had visited, Chapman was greeted as an old friend. He loved to come back in the spring. It was wonderful to see apple trees he had planted years before full of pink and white **blossoms.** But his greatest pleasure was to return in the fall when their **boughs** were weighed down with apples. Over the years he became a **familiar** sight to the people living on the farms and in the small towns of the Ohio River Valley. They gave him the **apt** name we know him by today—Johnny Appleseed.

▶ **Answer each of the following questions in the form of a sentence. If a question does not contain a vocabulary word from the lesson's word list, use one in your answer. Use each word only once.**

1. Why is Johnny Appleseed an **apt** name for John Chapman?

_____

_____

2. Why did people have reason to be grateful to Chapman?

_____

_____

3. How do we know Chapman was not vain about his appearance?

_____

_____

4. Why did Chapman refuse to eat meat?

_____

_____

5. How can we tell that John Chapman was not usually in a hurry?

_____

_____

6. What is the meaning of **practice** as it is used in the passage?

_____

_____

7. Where did Chapman get his apple seeds?

_____

_____

8. What did Chapman look for in materials to make a walking stick?

_____

_____

9. What did Chapman do at the end of the day when he was traveling?

_____

_____

apt
blossom
bough
content
detest
dusk
extinguish
familiar
obtain
orchard
practice
prune
stout
threadbare
wander

10. What did Chapman do if there was no one to give him a night's lodging?

_____

_____

11. Why did Chapman once put out his campfire?

_____

_____

12. What sight did Chapman enjoy in the spring?

_____

_____

13. Did the apple trees Chapman planted yield much fruit?

_____

_____

14. How do you know that Chapman often returned to places he had been to before?

_____

_____

15. Why did Chapman return to places where he had planted trees?

_____

_____

FUN & FASCINATING FACTS

- In Lesson 10, you learned that the word *orphan* comes from an old Sanskrit word. Another word that comes from this same language is **apt.** The Sanskrit word *apta* means "suitable" or "fitting." An *apt* remark is one that is a suitable or fitting thing to say.

- As an adjective, **content** means "satisfied." As a noun, it means "the amount contained." Then it is pronounced con'tent. (Don't drink water with high lead *content*.) The plural form, *contents,* means "all that is contained." (The bag spilled its *contents* onto the floor.)

Crossword Puzzle Solve the crossword puzzle by studying the clues and filling in the answer boxes. Clues followed by a number are definitions of words in Lessons 13 through 16. The number gives the word list in which the answer to the clue appears.

Clues Across

1. To defeat completely (13)
4. To believe without having proof (13)
8. To have and take pride in (14)
9. Several notes of music played together (14)
10. One of a group of mountains in Europe
11. Chairs go around it.
12. To put out, as a fire or a light (16)
13. Short for "Andrew"
16. In low spirits (13)
19. To beg; to ask for something (14)
20. The claw of a bird that hunts small animals (15)
24. Well-suited; fitting (16)
25. One, _____ , three
26. April, _____ , June
27. Not proud; modest (14)
28. To walk slowly and heavily (14)
29. It comes from bees.

Clues Down

2. To get by making an effort (16)
3. A prize or award (15)
4. Strong; not easily bent or broken (16)
5. To give careful thought to (15)
6. A state in the Midwest
7. To set apart (13)
9. Opposite of dirty
11. Shabby; worn out (16)
14. Lacking fun or excitement (13)
15. Satisfied with what one has (16)
17. Causing great sadness (13)
18. To dislike strongly (16)
19. Quick; without too much time passing (15)
21. Saudi _____ , a country in the Middle East
22. To cut off parts, especially branches (16)
23. A large branch of a tree (16)

Lesson **17**

For more practice and games, go to **www.WordlyWise3000.com**.

Word List	Study the definitions of the words. Then do the exercises that follow.

address
ə dres´

v. 1. To direct one's words to.
The head of the honor society **addressed** the whole student body.

2. To apply oneself to something.
As soon as Ms. Lu finishes solving one problem, she has to **address** a new one.

n. 1. A written or spoken speech.
President Lincoln scribbled the Gettysburg **Address** on an envelope.

2. (a´ dres) The place where someone lives or receives mail.
Let the post office know if you change your **address.**

approve
ə proov´

v. To think well of; to agree to.
My friend Lucia **approved** my choice of a dress for the party.

approval *n.* Thinking well of; agreeing to.
My parents' **approval** is important to me.

conclude
kən klood´

v. 1. To bring or come to an end.
It took us at least ten minutes to reach the exit after the concert **concluded.**

2. To form an opinion.
Jan **concluded** that mowing lawns was the best way to earn money next summer.

conclusion *n.* 1. The end.
A bow by the conductor marked the **conclusion** of the concert.

2. A judgment.
After talking to my teachers and my parents, I came to the **conclusion** that taking Spanish would be more useful to me than taking French.

deprive
di prīv´

v. To keep from having; to take away from.
The thunderstorm at 3:00 A.M. **deprived** me of a good night's sleep.

elder
el´dər

n. 1. A person who is older.
Sometimes we can learn a lot from our **elders** just by observing the way they live their lives.

2. Someone people look up to because of age and experience.
The **elders** of the village met to decide what to do about the increasing number of tourists.

adj. Older.
My **elder** brother is a senior in high school.

escort
es kôrt´

v. To travel with; to guide or protect a person.
When her husband was away, Anna asked her brother to **escort** her to the play.

n. (es´kôrt) One or more persons that escort.
The president always has a police **escort** when he travels by car.

fare
fer

n. 1. Money paid for a trip, by bus or train, for example.
What is the **fare** from Chicago to Orlando by air?

2. Food and drink.
The new restaurant serves Chinese **fare.**

v. To get along.
I wonder how my sister is **faring** on her mountain climbing trip.

forlorn
fôr lôrn´

adj. Sad and lonely.
Sam looked lost and **forlorn** as he sat waiting for his mother.

hearty
här´tē

adj. 1. Healthy; strong.
Grandpa liked to boast that at the age of eighty-five, he still had a **hearty** appetite at every meal.

2. Satisfying and full of flavor; tasty.
The **hearty** vegetable chili hit the spot on a cold day.

3. Friendly and enthusiastic.
Uncle Pete gave a **hearty** chuckle when my little brother told a joke.

inhale
in hāl´

v. To breathe in.
I tried to catch my breath by **inhaling** deeply several times.

merit me´rit	*v.* To deserve. The students' ideas for changes in the sports program **merit** careful study by the school board. *n.* Good qualities; worth. Dalal's teacher thought his fund-raising idea had **merit** and asked him to explain it to the class. **merits** *n. pl.* The actual facts. The judge said to forget what we'd heard on television and judge the case on its **merits**.
stingy stin´jē	*adj.* Not generous. Azania is too **stingy** to share her candy with anyone.
summon su´mən	*v.* 1. To call or send for. My father **summoned** me to the phone. 2. To call forth; to gather. I **summoned** all my courage and walked out on the stage.
valiant val´yənt	*adj.* Full of courage; brave. The firefighters were honored for their **valiant** deeds.
waft wäft	*v.* To move or be moved lightly over water or air; to drift. Petals from the cherry blossoms **wafted** over the path on the gentle breeze.

17A **Finding Meanings**

Choose two phrases to form a sentence that correctly uses a word from Word List 17. Write each sentence in the space provided.

1. (a) An address is   (c) time spent alone.
   (b) A fare is   (d) the money charged for a trip.

   _____

   _____

2. (a) breathe it in.   (c) To conclude something is to
   (b) do without it.   (d) To inhale something is to

   _____

   _____

3. (a) one that is enthusiastic.   (c) A forlorn expression is
   (b) one that shows agreement.   (d) A hearty laugh is

   _____

   _____

4. (a) The conclusion of a play is   (c) the beginning of it.
   (b) The merit of a play is   (d) the end of it.

   _____

   _____

5. (a) shun that person.   (c) To deprive someone is to
   (b) ask that person to come.   (d) To summon someone is to

   _____

   _____

6. (a) to be worthy of it.   (c) To be deprived of something is
   (b) To merit something is   (d) to value it.

   _____

   _____

7. (a) A person's approval is   (c) A person's address is
   (b) the place he lives.   (d) a feeling of distrust.

   _____

   _____

8. (a) Someone who is forlorn   (c) feels good about the future.
   (b) Someone who is valiant   (d) feels sad and lonely.

   _____

   _____

9. (a) a business partner.   (c) a wise, old person.
   (b) An escort is   (d) An elder is

   _____

   _____

10. (a) A stingy person is   (c) one who is full of courage.
    (b) A valiant person is   (d) one who is generous.

   _____

   _____

address
approve
conclude
deprive
elder
escort
fare
forlorn
hearty
inhale
merit
stingy
summon
valiant
waft

Improve each of the following sentences by crossing out the bold phrase and replacing it with a word (or a form of the word) from Word List 17.

1. The smell of freshly-mown hay **was carried by the breeze** across the meadow.

2. Trees that are **prevented from getting a supply** of proper nourishment will die.

3. The New Town Inn boasts that it offers the finest **food and drink** at the lowest prices in town.

4. My **view, after thinking about all the issues,** is that no real harm was done.

5. "Allow me to **stay beside you and walk with** you to your carriage," the gatekeeper said.

6. Samantha cannot marry without her parents' **agreement that she is doing the right thing.**

7. After such a **tasty and satisfying** meal, we all felt like taking naps.

8. They are so **unwilling to spend any more than they absolutely have to** that they expect me to babysit for fifty cents an hour.

9. The lawyer said that as long as the case is decided on its **facts as they are known,** her client will win.

10. Mayor Coffey **made a few remarks to** the people gathered outside City Hall, thanking them for their support.

Circle the letter or letters of each correct answer. A question may have more than one correct answer.

1. Which of the following can be **concluded?**
   - (a) a speech
   - (b) an agreement
   - (c) a meeting
   - (d) a project

2. Which of the following can **waft?**
   - (a) smoke
   - (b) smells
   - (c) stars
   - (d) hail

3. Which of the following can be **hearty?**
   - (a) a meal
   - (b) a greeting
   - (c) a storm
   - (d) an appetite

4. Which of the following show **approval?**
   - (a) turning thumbs down
   - (b) applauding
   - (c) cheering
   - (d) booing

5. Which of the following is a **valiant** act?
   - (a) giving up easily
   - (b) standing up for one's beliefs
   - (c) running away
   - (d) blaming someone else

6. Of which of the following can one be **deprived?**
   - (a) one's freedom
   - (b) one's rights
   - (c) one's good name
   - (d) one's business

7. Which of the following can be **addressed?**
   - (a) a meeting
   - (b) a person
   - (c) a package
   - (d) a nation

8. Which of the following can be **inhaled?**
   - (a) air
   - (b) food
   - (c) steam
   - (d) music

address
approve
conclude
deprive
elder
escort
fare
forlorn
hearty
inhale
merit
stingy
summon
valiant
waft

Words that sound the same but have different meanings and/or spellings are called homophones. *To, too,* and *two* are homophones; so are *ate* and *eight.* The form of humor called a pun depends on homophones. Here's an example: Why is *six* afraid of *seven*? Answer: Because *seven eight* (ate) *nine.*

Decide which word in each homophone pair best fits each sentence. Write the word in the blank.

hail / hale

1. The rain turned to _____ as the temperature fell.

2. He was over ninety, but looked as _____ as ever.

peer / pier

3. We joined the fishermen at the end of the _____.

4. I had to stand on tiptoe to _____ into the room.

vain / vein

5. A _____ carries blood to the heart.

6. A _____ person loves to be flattered.

bore / boar

7. I used a drill to _____ the hole.

8. A male pig is called a _____.

fare / fair

9. The bus _____ to Hoboken is ten dollars.

10. The county _____ begins this Saturday.

chord / cord

11. Jonah played a _____ on his guitar.

12. We tied the bundle of wood with a length of _____.

bough / bow

13. Every _____ of the tree was full of apples.

14. The Japanese greet strangers with a polite _____.

Read the passage. Then answer the questions that follow it.

An African Folktale

Some folktales tell of **valiant** deeds performed by great heroes; an example is the Japanese story of Tokoyo and the sea monster. Others explain how things came to be. The Welsh tale of the silver cows and the water lilies is one such story. A third group tells how the weak and helpless defeat the strong and powerful. This does not always happen in real life, but it does happen in folktales. An example is this East African story of the *maskini* and the *tajiri*.

Every evening, the *tajiri*, or rich man, sat down to a **hearty** meal prepared for him in his own kitchen. The food that was left over would have been enough to feed a whole family. But the *tajiri* was extremely **stingy.** The leftovers from his table went to his pigs to fatten them up for later use.

The *maskini*, or poor man, lived on simple **fare.** He owned a goat that gave him milk and cheese, but his evening meal was usually nothing more than a bowl of porridge. However, he had found a way to make it more enjoyable. He would eat his meal while hidden outside the *tajiri*'s kitchen. There, wonderful smells came **wafting** through the open window. They made the *maskini*'s mouth water, so the simple porridge seemed like a feast.

One evening, the *tajiri* decided to take a walk in his garden to work up an appetite for dinner. He saw the *maskini* sitting outside the kitchen window. As the *tajiri* watched, he saw the *maskini* **inhale** deeply. A blissful look came over the poor man's face. How dare he help himself to my smells, thought the *tajiri*. He ordered his servants to seize the *maskini* and **escort** him to the village jail.

A few days later, the *maskini* was **summoned** before the court that met weekly in the village center. The village elders would decide the case on its **merits.** The *tajiri* explained that the smells from the kitchen belonged to him; the *maskini* was **depriving** him of them. As payment, he demanded the *maskini*'s goat, which was the only thing he owned. When asked to respond, the *maskini*, looking very **forlorn,** could only stare at the ground and shuffle his feet, afraid to speak. The village **elders** now withdrew to the shade of a nearby baobab tree. After a brief discussion, the village chief came forward and **addressed** the crowd.

"The *maskini* did help himself to the smells from the *tajiri*'s kitchen," she said. "However, he did not receive any food from him. We have **concluded,**

address
approve
conclude
deprive
elder
escort
fare
forlorn
hearty
inhale
merit
stingy
summon
valiant
waft

therefore, that the *tajiri* should not be given the goat. However, in fairness to him we believe he should have the right to smell the *maskini*'s goat whenever he wants."

The *tajiri* was furious. He left without saying a word. But the people of the village **approved** the court's decision. They felt that justice had been done.

▶ **Answer each of the following questions in the form of a sentence. If a question does not contain a vocabulary word from the lesson's word list, use one in your answer. Use each word only once.**

1. Did the *maskini* put up a **valiant** defense in the court?

_____

_____

2. What is the meaning of **hearty** as it is used in the passage?

_____

_____

3. The story says the *tajiri* was **stingy.** How does it show this?

_____

_____

4. How did the *tajiri* **fare** when he went to court?

_____

_____

5. What would have happened if the kitchen window had been closed?

_____

_____

6. How did the *tajiri* know that the *maskini* was enjoying the smells from the kitchen?

_____

_____

7. Why did the *maskini* need an **escort?**

_____

_____

8. Did the *maskini* have to go to court?

_____

_____

9. What does it mean to say the case would be decided on its **merits?**

_____

_____

10. Had the *maskini* taken anything from the *tajiri?*

_____

_____

11. Why do you think the *maskini* looked **forlorn?**

_____

_____

12. What sort of person might become one of the village **elders?**

_____

_____

13. To whom did the chief direct her remarks?

_____

_____

14. What is the meaning of **concluded** as it is used in the passage?

_____

_____

15. How might the crowd have shown that it **approved** of the court's decision?

_____

_____

address
approve
conclude
deprive
elder
escort
fare
forlorn
hearty
inhale
merit
stingy
summon
valiant
waft

- President Lincoln gave a famous speech at Gettysburg in 1863 that begins, "Four score and seven years ago." Why do we refer to it as the Gettysburg **Address** rather than the Gettysburg Speech? One reason is that *address* suggests something grander and more important than a speech. Anyone can make a speech, but you have to be someone important and the occasion a special one for it to be called an address.

- **Fare** and *fair* are homophones. They sound exactly the same but have different meanings and spellings. *Fair* is an adjective with several meanings and is also a noun, as visitors to a county *fair* know very well.

- As an adjective, **elder** means "greater than another in age or seniority." If we refer to someone greatest in age or seniority, we use *eldest*. (Mark is my *elder* brother. He is not the *eldest*.) (Sheila is the *eldest* of six children.) *Elder* and *eldest* are used when referring to persons. *Older* and *oldest* can refer either to persons or things.

- We turn many words into their opposites simply by changing the prefix. **Inhale** means "to breathe in." It is made up of the prefix *in-*, meaning "in" and the root formed from the Latin verb *halare*, meaning "to breathe." By knowing that the prefix *ex-* means "out," you can turn *inhale* into its opposite and make a word that means "to breathe out." What is that word?

For more practice and games, go to **www.WordlyWise3000.com**.

Word List

Study the definitions of the words. Then do the exercises that follow.

abreast
ə brest´

adj. or *adv.* 1. Side-by-side.
We walked three **abreast,** except where the path was so narrow that we had to walk single file.

2. Up-to-date.
I try to stay **abreast** of what is happening in the world by reading the paper every day.

barrier
bar´ē ər

n. Anything that stops progress or blocks the way.
Lack of education is often a **barrier** to success in life.

breadth
bredth

n. 1. The distance of something from side to side; width.
The arrow missed the target by no more than a hand's **breadth.**

2. Wide range; largeness.
Carlos got the job because of his **breadth** of experience.

capital
ka´ pə tl

n. 1. Wealth that can be used to produce more wealth.
You don't need much **capital** to buy that pizza business.

2. The city where the government of a state or country is located.
The **capital** of Montana is Helena.

adj. Punishable by death.
Murder is a **capital** crime in many states.

ensure
in shoor´

v. To make sure or certain.
Wearing a seat belt will help **ensure** your safety in case of an accident.

external
ek stʉr´ nəl

adj. On or related to the outside.
The **external** walls of the house are covered with shingles as protection.

feud
fyōōd

n. A long, bitter quarrel, especially one between two families.
It took the tragic deaths of Romeo and Juliet to end the **feud** between their two families.

v. To be enemies, to quarrel.
The Hatfields and the McCoys **feuded** for years.

fortress
fôr´ trəs

n. A building with strong walls made to be defended against attack; a fort.
Rather than attack the **fortress** directly, the invaders went around it.

frequent
frē´kwənt

adj. Happening often or over and over.
My mother's business requires her to make **frequent** visits to Japan.

v. To go to over and over.
We **frequent** the local bakery regularly for oatmeal cookies.

frequency   *n.* The number of times something is repeated.
My clarinet playing improved with the **frequency** of my practicing.

---

frontier
frun tīr´

n. 1. The line between two countries.
We said goodbye to France and crossed the **frontier** into Spain in the early morning.

2. The outer limits of the settled part of a country.
The American **frontier** moved slowly westward in the nineteenth century.

3. The outer limits of knowledge.
The **frontiers** of medicine are being pushed back at a rapidly increasing rate.

---

peasant
pez´ ənt

n. A person who makes a living from working the soil, especially in poorer countries.
The **Peasants'** Revolt in England in 1381 was a shock to the government.

---

petty
pe´ tē

adj. Of little importance; small.
A **petty** disagreement over a parking space led to a bitter quarrel between them.

---

threat
thret

n. A warning that one may do harm.
Olivia tried to quiet her dog after her neighbor's **threat** to call the police.

threaten   *v.* To make a threat.
My brother **threatened** to tell my mother that I ate all the cake.

threatening   *adj.* Suggesting harm or danger.
The dark clouds looked very **threatening.**

---

utilize
yoo´ tl īz

v. To put to use.
We **utilized** whatever scraps of fabric we had to make a costume.

---

vast
vast

adj. Very great in area or amount.
The Pacific Ocean is a **vast** body of water.

Choose two phrases to form a sentence that correctly uses a word from Word List 18. Write each sentence in the space provided.

1. (a) The breadth of something is
   (b) the number of times it occurs.
   (c) The frequency of something is
   (d) its unexpected absence.

   _____

   _____

2. (a) A frontier is
   (b) A barrier is
   (c) a person who makes a living from the soil.
   (d) the outer limits of the settled part of a country.

   _____

   _____

3. (a) Capital is
   (b) severe punishment.
   (c) Breadth is
   (d) distance from side to side.

   _____

   _____

4. (a) to have knowledge of it.
   (b) to avoid it.
   (c) To be abreast of something is
   (d) To ensure something is

   _____

   _____

5. (a) is punishable by death.
   (b) goes unpunished.
   (c) A petty crime is one that
   (d) A capital crime is one that

   _____

   _____

6. (a) something that blocks the way.
   (b) something that can be used.
   (c) A peasant is
   (d) A barrier is

   _____

   _____

abreast
barrier
breadth
capital
ensure
external
feud
fortress
frequent
frontier
peasant
petty
threat
utilize
vast

7. (a) A vast army   (c) is one that has been routed.
   (b) is one about to attack.   (d) A threatening army

_____

_____

8. (a) A fortress is   (c) a person who makes a living from the soil.
   (b) A peasant is   (d) a humble cottage.

_____

_____

9. (a) A petty difference is   (c) one that keeps increasing.
   (b) one of little importance.   (d) A vast difference is

_____

_____

10. (a) A fortress is   (c) A feud is
    (b) a bitter quarrel.   (d) the line between two countries.

_____

_____

11. (a) make sure it happens.   (c) To ensure something is to
    (b) make sure it doesn't happen.   (d) To utilize something is to

_____

_____

Improve each of the following sentences by crossing out the bold phrase and replacing it with a word (or a form of the word) from Word List 18.

1. My father **puts to good use** every leftover when he makes a casserole.

2. A **building that is made to be defended against attack** should be built on high ground.

3. A country needs **wealth that can be used to produce more wealth** in order to produce jobs.

4. The points Eric raised were so **lacking in importance** that everyone ignored them.

5. If you try to **suggest that you could be a danger to** me, I won't talk to you anymore.

6. I know most of the people who **make regular visits to** the Cosy Cafe; I have lunch there every day.

7. Most streets aren't wide enough for three cyclists riding **side by side.**

8. The land of the former Soviet Union is so **great in the area it covers** that it crosses nine time zones.

9. The first symptoms of measles are **on the outside and show up on the skin.**

10. Many of the **lines separating the various countries** of Europe were redrawn after the First World War.

11. The two families continued to **keep up the long and bitter quarrel** because neither side was willing to give in.

abreast
barrier
breadth
capital
ensure
external
feud
fortress
frequent
frontier
peasant
petty
threat
utilize
vast

Circle the letter or letters of each correct answer. A question may have more than one correct answer.

1. Which of the following has **breadth?**
   - (a) a surface
   - (b) a point where lines meet
   - (c) a brick
   - (d) a line joining two points

2. Which of the following is an **external** symptom?
   - (a) a sore throat
   - (b) a stomach ache
   - (c) a skin rash
   - (d) a twitching eyelid

3. In which of the following places are you likely to find a **peasant?**
   - (a) a city
   - (b) a farm
   - (c) an office
   - (d) a field

4. Which of the following is a **threatening** remark?
   - (a) "See you later."
   - (b) "I'll get even with you!"
   - (c) "You'll be sorry."
   - (d) "I'm sorry."

5. Which of the following would be considered **vast?**
   - (a) the Atlantic Ocean
   - (b) the distance to the nearest star
   - (c) the universe
   - (d) the American prairie

6. Which of the following is a **capital?**
   - (a) Washington, D.C.
   - (b) Paris, France
   - (c) Ottawa, Canada
   - (d) Bronx, New York

7. Which of the following are **petty** concerns?
   - (a) your choice of breakfast cereal
   - (b) your choice of school
   - (c) a broken fingernail
   - (d) a broken leg

8. Which of the following do people change **frequently?**
   - (a) their date of birth
   - (b) their socks
   - (c) their eating habits
   - (d) their names

Write the antonym of each word on the left in the space next to it. Choose from the words on the right, which are in a different order.

1. stingy _____ cowardly

2. familiar _____ generous

3. approve _____ start

4. stout _____ blissful

5. frequent _____ resist

6. extinguish _____ exciting

7. submit _____ tiny

8. conclude _____ reject

9. dreary _____ light

10. valiant _____ fragile

11. vast _____ strange

12. forlorn _____ rare

Read the passage. Then answer the questions that follow it.

The Great Wall of China

Most visitors to China make a point of seeing the Great Wall. It is hard to miss because of its enormous size. The wall is about twenty-five feet high. Its **breadth** at the top is nearly twenty feet. That's wide enough for ten people to walk **abreast.** It covers a distance of fifteen hundred miles. The wall starts in Gansu province in the south and ends at the Yellow Sea in the northeast. The part tourists visit most **frequently** goes from Beijing, the **capital** of China, to the Yellow Sea.

The Great Wall of China was built more than two thousand years ago. It served as a **barrier** against tribes from the north. The person responsible for having it built was Shi Huangdi, known as "the First Emperor of China." Before the country was united under his leadership, China was divided into a large number of **petty** kingdoms. They were ruled by local warlords who spent most of their time **feuding** among themselves. By the year 221 B.C.E., Shi Huangdi had taken control of the whole country and made himself emperor.

Because the empire was so **vast,** it was not easy to defend. Shi Huangdi had nothing to fear at home. However, he worried about **external** attacks. Especially **threatening** were tribes from the north in central Asia. To **ensure** the safety of his empire, he had the Great Wall built along China's northern **frontier.** It had watchtowers every few miles. It also had **fortresses.** The emperor's soldiers were housed there, ready to fight off attacks. Building began in 214 B.C.E. Later rulers of China added to it in the west and south. Work on the wall was still being carried out four centuries ago.

Hundreds of thousands of Chinese **peasants** were forced to leave their farms to do the actual work of building the Great Wall. Everything had to be carried on the workers' backs or slung on poles; the wheelbarrow had not yet been invented. The builders **utilized** whatever was close at hand. They used blocks of stone in mountain areas and timber from forests. In other places, they used earth or sand mixed with twigs and reeds. Later on, bricks and tiles were used.

Shi Huangdi is an important figure in Chinese history. He improved the workings of government. He also ordered the building of roads and canals to improve communications throughout the empire. He built a magnificent palace as well as many other fine public buildings. But his greatest achievement, and the thing for which he is remembered, is the Great Wall of China.

▶ **Answer each of the following questions in the form of a sentence. If a question does not contain a vocabulary word from the lesson's word list, use one in your answer. Use each word only once.**

1. Why do you think tourists visit the Great Wall so **frequently?**

_____

_____

2. Why does it take a very long time to cross China?

_____

_____

3. Why would you expect to find many government offices in Beijing?

_____

_____

4. Why did the "First Emperor" build the Great Wall?

_____

_____

5. What enemies was Shi Huangdi worried about?

_____

_____

6. How did the local warlords get along with each other?

_____

_____

7. How much influence do you think the ruler of a **petty** kingdom would have?

_____

_____

abreast
barrier
breadth
capital
ensure
external
feud
fortress
frequent
frontier
peasant
petty
threat
utilize
vast

8. Why was Shi Huangdi concerned about the tribes in Central Asia?

_____

_____

9. Where would an invasion of China by the northern tribes have taken place?

_____

_____

10. What materials did the builders of the wall use?

_____

_____

11. What was the purpose of the **fortresses** that were built into the wall?

_____

_____

12. Why was it possible to use the top of the Great Wall as a road?

_____

_____

13. Why would the Great Wall be easy to see from the air?

_____

_____

14. Why might the **peasants** have resented having to work on the wall?

_____

_____

15. Was the Great Wall successful in doing what it was supposed to do?

_____

_____

FUN & FASCINATING FACTS

- Don't confuse the word **capital,** which has several meanings as an adjective and is also a noun, with the word *capitol,* which is a noun only.

  The *Capitol* (with an uppercase *C*) is the building in which the United States Congress meets. A *capitol* (with a lowercase *c*) is the building in which the governing body of a state meets. It might help you to remember the difference between *capital* and *capitol* if you note that most *capitols* are buildings with *domes,* a word with an *o* in it.

- **External** refers to that which is outside, rather than inside. Its antonym, *internal,* refers to that which is inside rather than outside. The skin is the body's only *external* organ. The heart, lungs, liver, and kidneys are *internal* organs.

  A related word to *external* is *exterior;* its antonym is *interior.* An *exterior* door is one on the outside; an *interior* door is one inside a building that connects one room with another.

For more practice and games, go to www.WordlyWise3000.com.

Word List	Study the definitions of the words. Then do the exercises that follow.

audition
ô dish´ ən

n. A short performance by an actor or musician as a test for a particular job.
Auditions for the school band will be held tomorrow.

v. To try out for.
Six people **auditioned** for the part of Helen Keller in the fourth-grade play.

create
krē āt´

v. To bring into being; to produce for the first time.
The computer industry has **created** many new jobs.

creative *adj.* Having new and original ideas.
Mozart was one of the most **creative** musicians that ever lived.

creation *n.* The act of bringing into being; something created.
The **creation** of three new teaching positions means that classrooms will be less crowded.

elevate
e´ lə vāt

v. To lift up; to raise to a higher level.
Jane Austen **elevated** the English novel to new heights.

elevation (e´ lə vā´ shən) *n.* Height.
I have to look up the **elevation** of Mt. Monadnock for my chart.

eliminate
i li´ mə nāt

v. To get rid of; to remove or leave out.
Zeb decided to **eliminate** the last paragraph because his report was too long.

elimination (i li mə na´ shən) *n.* A getting rid of.
The **elimination** of the Red Sox from the pennant race upset my mother terribly.

engage
in gāj´

v. 1. To put to work; to hire.
The Beachfront Restaurant **engages** extra help every summer.

2. To keep busy or active.
Wen Lin tried to **engage** her cousin in conversation, but she was very shy.

3. To bind oneself to do something, especially to marry.
My parents got **engaged** on New Year's Eve.

entrance
in trans´

v. To fill with joy or delight.
The young dancers **entranced** the audience with their grace and beauty.

entrancing *adj.* Delightful.
The songs were so **entrancing** that we hated to see the performance end.

essential e sen´shəl	*adj.* Most important; very necessary. Fresh fruit and vegetables are **essential** to a good diet. **essentials** *n. pl.* Something that cannot be done without. I packed my overnight bag with my toothbrush and other **essentials.**
foremost fôr´mōst	*adj.* First in importance, time, or place. This new play by America's **foremost** playwright is breaking all box office records.
forsake fôr sāk´	*v.* To have nothing more to do with; to turn one's back on. I'd never **forsake** my old friends if I became rich and famous.
recognize re´kig nīz	*v.* 1. To know and remember upon seeing. I **recognized** the name, but not the face. 2. To admit the truth or accept the existence of. For many years, the U.S. was unwilling to **recognize** the government of China. 3. To accept and approve. The manager told my mother that the company **recognizes** the good job she does.
sentimental sen tə men´tl	*adj.* Expressing feelings of love or pity, sometimes to excess. The movie was so **sentimental** that everyone was in tears.
source sôrs	*n.* The thing or place from which something comes. We decided to go on a trip to reach the **source** of the Nile River.
tour toor	*n.* A trip or journey in which one usually returns to the starting point. The band played over twenty concerts on its **tour** of the Midwest. *v.* To travel to different places. My cousin Anna and I **toured** the old part of Montreal in a horse-drawn carriage.
tradition trə dish´ən	*n.* A belief, custom, or usual way of doing things, handed down within families or other groups. Fireworks on July 4 are an American **tradition.** **traditional** *adj.* Handed down from age to age. My whole family enjoys getting together for a **traditional** Passover seder.
trio trē´ō	*n.* A group of three people. Luis plays the cello in a **trio.**

Choose two phrases to form a sentence that correctly uses a word from Word List 19. Write each sentence in the space provided.

1. (a) the things that are left out.   (c) Essentials are
   (b) Traditions are   (d) the things considered necessary.

   _____

   _____

2. (a) know or remember it.   (c) To create a piece of work is to
   (b) To recognize a piece of   (d) make changes in it.
       work is to

   _____

   _____

3. (a) passed down over time.   (c) that is no longer practiced.
   (b) A traditional custom is one   (d) A sentimental custom is one

   _____

   _____

4. (a) A creation is   (c) a small group.
   (b) A tour is   (d) something produced for the
                                            first time.

   _____

   _____

5. (a) to consider.   (c) to delight.
   (b) To entrance is   (d) To audition is

   _____

   _____

6. (a) turn one's back on that person. (c) To engage someone is to
   (b) protect that person.   (d) To forsake someone is to

   _____

   _____

7. (a) Elimination of something is
   (b) finding a new and different use for it.
   (c) Elevation of something is
   (d) getting rid of it.

_____

_____

8. (a) To audition someone is to
   (b) To engage someone is to
   (c) hire that person.
   (d) get rid of that person.

_____

_____

9. (a) a journey around a place.
   (b) the answer to a puzzle.
   (c) A source is
   (d) A tour is

_____

_____

audition

create

elevate

eliminate

engage

entrance

essential

foremost

forsake

recognize

sentimental

source

tour

tradition

trio

**Improve each of the following sentences by crossing out the bold phrase
and replacing it with a word (or a form of the word) from Word List 19.**

1. Stephen Hawking is one of the world's **greatest and most important**
   experts on black holes.

2. At my parents' anniversary party, a **group of three singers** sang
   popular songs from the sixties and seventies.

3. We were able to locate the **place that was the beginning** of the river
   by following it and hiking up to the mountains.

4. The Pied Piper's job was to **get rid of** the rats from the town of
   Hamelin.

5. My cousin Becca and Juan Morales, her friend from grade school,
   became **promised to each other in marriage** on June 1.

6. Because I am so short, I have to **put at a higher level** every piano stool
   I sit on.

7. I always cry at weddings because I'm so **easily affected by romantic
   feelings.**

8. Sequoya **brought into being for the first time** a written language for
   the Cherokee people.

9. The government **admits the existence of** the need for laws to protect
   the wetlands.

10. The **short performances that people gave who were trying out** for
    the orchestra lasted all day.

11. We returned again and again to Trinidad because the island is so
    delightful and pleasurable.

Circle the letter or letters of each correct answer. A question may have more than one correct answer.

1. Which of the following might one **audition** for?
   (a) a job with a band
   (b) an apartment rental
   (c) a part in a play
   (d) a factory position

2. Which of the following is **essential** for college?
   (a) graduation from high school
   (b) being on a sports team
   (c) a passport
   (d) good grades

3. Which of the following are birthday **traditions?**
   (a) blowing out candles
   (b) having cake
   (c) getting presents
   (d) making pumpkin pie

4. Which of the following might one **tour?**
   (a) a precipice
   (b) a museum
   (c) an address
   (d) a film studio

5. Which of the following might one **forsake?**
   (a) one's friends
   (b) one's family
   (c) one's career
   (d) one's height

6. Which of the following might **elevate** one's spirits?
   (a) being hailed by a friend
   (b) a pessimistic remark
   (c) being jeered by a crowd
   (d) finishing a lot of work

7. Which of the following might **entrance** a child?
   (a) a red balloon
   (b) a boring tale
   (c) a funny clown
   (d) a threatening gesture

8. Which should one **eliminate** for good health?
   (a) a balanced diet
   (b) regular check-ups
   (c) eating fatty foods
   (d) exercise

audition
create
elevate
eliminate
engage
entrance
essential
foremost
forsake
recognize
sentimental
source
tour
tradition
trio

> The prefix *tri-* means "three" and comes from both Greek and Latin. A *triceratops* is a large, three-horned dinosaur. But the letters *tri* at the beginning of a word do not always function as a prefix. Sometimes a word just happens to begin with these three letters.

Look at each word and its meaning and decide if *tri* is a prefix in that word. If it is, underline the first three letters. If it isn't, don't underline anything.

1. triangle   a figure with three straight sides

2. trillion   a thousand billion

3. triplets   three babies born at a single birth

4. trial   a case heard in a court of law

5. tricycle   a child's bike with three wheels

6. trident   a three-pointed spear

7. tricolor   the red, white, and blue French flag

8. trio   a group of three

9. tribe   a group of families ruled by a chief

10. triplicate   made in three copies

11. tripod   a three-legged stand

12. trickle   to flow slowly in a thin stream

Read the passage. Then answer the questions that follow it.

Martha Graham: Artist and Teacher

Martha Graham was one of the **foremost** dancers of the twentieth century. She founded a dance company that performed modern dance for an ever-widening audience. She was also **recognized** as one of the greatest teachers of modern dance.

Before Martha Graham's time, dance as a serious art form meant French and Russian ballet. Ballet had remained largely unchanged since the nineteenth century. It told stories that were often **sentimental** and far removed from the real world. The dance steps followed fixed patterns of movement. Female dancers wore **traditional** tight-waisted costumes with short skirts and tights. Their stiffened ballet shoes enabled them to dance on their toes. Music was usually classical. It was often written especially for the ballet.

Martha Graham began by **eliminating** from her dances everything that she felt was unnecessary. What remained was a new kind of dance, stripped to its **essentials.** It used bare stage settings and the simplest of costumes. Her dancers were usually barefoot and wore loose, flowing clothes. Her subjects were drawn from a great variety of **sources.** They included Native American life, American history, and the poetry of Emily Dickinson. She tried to develop a kind of dance that expressed human feelings along with telling a story.

Martha Graham's lifelong interest in dance began in 1912. At the age of seventeen, she saw Ruth St. Denis perform in San Francisco as part of her American **tour.** St. Denis was heavily influenced by Japanese, Indian, and Spanish dances. Graham was **entranced** by what she saw. She began taking dancing lessons. When she was twenty-two, she successfully **auditioned** for the Denishawn dance company. The company was run by Ruth St. Denis and her husband, Ted Shawn. Graham stayed with the company for seven years. She became one of its leading dancers.

In 1924, Martha Graham decided to **forsake** the life of a performer for a while. She concentrated on teaching and developing her own style of dancing. Two years later she returned to the New York stage. Graham brought with her a **trio** of female dancers who had been her best students; in 1930 she formed the much larger Martha Graham Dance Company. She preferred women dancers; not until 1938 did she **engage** male dancers to

audition
create
elevate
eliminate
engage
entrance
essential
foremost
forsake
recognize
sentimental
source
tour
tradition
trio

appear on stage with her. "Modern dance," she once said, "isn't anything in my mind except one thing—the freedom of women in America."

Her last public performance took place in 1969, when she was seventy-four years old. She had won over all her critics; she had **elevated** modern dance to a new American art form. When she died in 1991, she was at work **creating** a new dance for her company. Martha Graham was ninety-six years old. That unfinished work, *The Eyes of the Goddess*, was performed by her company shortly after her death. The performance was a tribute to one of America's greatest artists.

▶ **Answer each of the following questions in the form of a sentence. If a question does not contain a vocabulary word from the lesson's word list, use one in your answer. Use each word only once.**

1. How do people around the country get to see dance companies?

_____

_____

2. How did Martha Graham change the style of dance?

_____

_____

3. What were **traditional** costumes like?

_____

_____

4. How would you describe the Martha Graham stage?

_____

_____

5. What were French and Russian ballet like?

_____

_____

6. Where did Martha Graham get ideas for her dances?

_____

_____

7. How did Martha Graham feel about Ruth St. Denis's performance?

_____

_____

8. Why did Martha Graham **forsake** performing in 1924?

_____

_____

9. What is the meaning of **engage** as it is used in the passage?

_____

_____

10. Martha Graham brought a **trio** of dancers to the New York stage. How many dancers is that?

_____

_____

11. What is the meaning of **recognized** as it is used in the passage?

_____

_____

12. What was Martha Graham doing at the time of her death?

_____

_____

13. What does the passage seem to regard as Martha Graham's greatest achievement?

_____

_____

14. Why is Martha Graham famous?

_____

_____

15. What do you have to do to get into a dance company?

_____

_____

audition
create
elevate
eliminate
engage
entrance
essential
foremost
forsake
recognize
sentimental
source
tour
tradition
trio

- If you **audition** for a part in a play, you want to make sure that you are *heard*. The word itself suggests this; it comes from the Latin verb *audire*, which means "to hear." Other words formed from this root include the following:

Audible, loud enough to be heard (an *audible* whisper);

Audio, intended to be heard (an *audio* tape);

Audience, a group of people gathered together to hear (and also to see) whatever is being performed for their enjoyment;

Auditorium, a large room in which people come together to hear a presentation;

Auditory, having to do with the ear (the *auditory* nerve).

- A **trio** is a group of three, especially a group of three musicians or other entertainers. The word comes from the Latin (and Greek) word for "three." Other Latin numbers give us the following: *duet,* two performers or a piece to be performed by two persons, from the Latin *duo; quartet,* a group of four, from the Latin *quattuor; quintet,* a group of five, from the Latin *quintus; sextet,* a group of six, from the Latin *sex; septet,* a group of seven, from the Latin *septem;* and *octet,* a group of eight, from the Latin *octo.*

Entrance has two pronunciations: en 'transs, and 'en trənss. The more common pronunciation, 'en trənss, means "a way to go inside someplace or something." En 'transs, "to fill with joy or delight," which appears in this lesson, is less common.

Lesson **20**

For more practice and games, go
to **www.WordlyWise3000.com**.

Word List	Study the definitions of the words. Then do the exercises that follow.

arrest
ə rest´

v. 1. To stop the movement or progress of.
The doctors were able to **arrest** the spread of the disease.

2. To seize and charge with breaking the law.
When the police **arrested** the suspect, they found the stolen jewelry in his pocket!

n. The act of arresting.
The police officer made the **arrest** at the scene of the crime.

capable
kā´ pə bəl

adj. Able to do things well; skilled.
Companies try to hire the most **capable** workers.

capable of 1. Ready and able to.
Even in his nineties, Bob Hope was still **capable of** entertaining an audience.

2. Having the qualities necessary for.
Although she's only fourteen, Samantha is **capable of** babysitting two small children.

congratulate
kən gra´ chə lāt

v. To express pleasure for a person's success or good fortune.
Allow me to **congratulate** you on your victory.

congratulations (kən gra chə lā´ shəns) *n. pl.* Good wishes.
Our class made Zel a card that said, "**Congratulations** on winning the 10K race!"

despise
di spīz´

v. To scorn and dislike strongly; to consider unworthy of respect.
The French nobles **despised** the peasants, whom they considered lacking in refinement.

dispute
di spyo͞ot´

n. A strong difference of opinion; an argument.
The feuding neighbors were unable to settle their **dispute** and finally took it to court.

v. To question the truth or value of.
When her parents **disputed** the value of her new bike, Rona produced an article in *Cycling* that praised it.

eventual
i ven´ cho͞o əl

adj. Coming at a later time; happening as a result of.
Years of practice led to his **eventual** success as a Wimbledon tennis champion.

| **helm**
helm | *n.* 1. The wheel or tiller used to steer a boat.
The skipper said I could take the **helm** since the sea was calm. |
| | 2. A position of control.
With a new president at the **helm,** the company should grow. |

| **humiliate**
hyŏō mi´ lē ăt | *v.* To treat in a way that takes away a person's pride or self respect.
His fellow workers **humiliated** Hans Christian Andersen because he seemed so strange. |
| | **humiliation** (hyŏō mi´ lē ā´ shən) *n.* The act of humiliating or the state of being humiliated.
The emperor in the story could not hide his **humiliation** at the way the two "tailors" had tricked him. |

| **implore**
im plôr´ | *v.* To plead with or beg for with much feeling.
I **implored** my parents to let me go with them. |

| **insert**
in sʉrt´ | *v.* To put in.
"Please **insert** fifty-five cents," said the voice on the phone. |
| | *n.* (in´ sʉrt) An extra piece sewn or put in place.
My new shirt has a lace **insert** at the neck. |

outrage out´ rāj	*n.* 1. Anger caused by injury or insult. The decision to close the school caused **outrage** among the parents.
	2. Anything that causes resentment or anger; a wicked or brutal act or remark. "Capital punishment is an **outrage** and should be banned!" she shouted.
	v. To fill with anger or resentment. The way some people allow their dogs to run without a leash **outrages** me.

pierce pirs	*v.* 1. To pass or break through. A beam of light suddenly **pierced** the darkness.
	2. To make a hole through. The needle **pierced** the thick fabric easily.
	piercing *adj.* Very loud and shrill. The **piercing** cries of the seagulls woke me up.

quiver kwi´ vər	*v.* To shake with small, rapid movements; to tremble. The child's lip **quivered** as if he were about to cry.
	n. 1. A trembling. There was a **quiver** in her voice as Mira told us about the accident.
	2. A case for holding arrows. Each archer was equipped with a bow and a **quiver** full of arrows.

release	*v.* 1. To let go; to free.
ri lēs´	The pigeons flew away as soon as I **released** them from their cages.
	2. To make known.
	A copy of the governor's speech was **released** to reporters at noon.
	n. 1. A setting free.
	Four years after his **release** from prison, Nelson Mandela was sworn in as South Africa's first black president.
	2. An announcement of news.
	The governor's office sent a press **release** about the new program.

| sullen | *adj.* Silent from anger or hurt. |
| su´lən | Tom grew from a **sullen** teenager into a friendly and outgoing young man. |

20A ▷ Finding Meanings

Choose two phrases to form a sentence that correctly uses a word from Word List 20. Write each sentence in the space provided.

1. (a) A quiver is
   (b) A release is
   (c) an extra piece put into place.
   (d) a case for arrows.

_____

_____

2. (a) A capable person is one who
   (b) whose self-respect has been lost.
   (c) An outraged person is one
   (d) is able to do things well.

_____

_____

3. (a) a rapid shaking movement.
   (b) An arrest is
   (c) A quiver is
   (d) a putting off until later.

_____

_____

4. (a) to deny that it is true.
   (b) To insert a story is
   (c) to announce it.
   (d) To release a story is

_____

_____

arrest
capable
congratulate
despise
dispute
eventual
helm
humiliate
implore
insert
outrage
pierce
quiver
release
sullen

5. (a) An arrest is

    (b) A dispute is

    (c) a stopping by an officer of the law.

    (d) a changing of one's mind.

_____

_____

6. (a) To humiliate someone is to

    (b) plead with that person.

    (c) make that person very angry.

    (d) To implore someone is to

_____

_____

7. (a) a sudden stop.

    (b) an argument.

    (c) A dispute is

    (d) A helm is

_____

_____

8. (a) is silently angry.

    (b) thinks fondly of the past.

    (c) A sullen person is one who

    (d) A humiliated person is one who

_____

_____

9. (a) to shock and anger that person.

    (b) to think highly of that person.

    (c) To despise someone is

    (d) To outrage someone is

_____

_____

10. (a) something that is removed.

    (b) An insert is

    (c) an extra piece put in place.

    (d) A helm is

_____

_____

Improve each of the following sentences by crossing out the bold phrase and replacing it with a word (or a form of the word) from Word List 20.

1. Her high soprano voice suddenly **broke through** the silence of the auditorium.

2. They'll come around to your way of thinking **sooner or later.**

3. Jeff was almost in tears as he **begged and pleaded with** me to help him with his math homework.

4. Unlike her cheerful sister, Noa had a **dark and gloomy** nature.

5. Six quarters must be **put into the slot** before the washing machine will start.

6. I **questioned the correctness of** the price I was charged because the sign said "Everything Half-Price."

7. **"Good wishes,"** said Mr. Singh. "You did a great job."

8. My **loss of pride in what I was doing** was so great when the audience didn't even applaud that I rushed off the stage.

9. Nan and Johanna took turns at the **wheel used to steer the boat** on their tour of the islands.

10. Annabel will do a good job building the new bathroom because she is so **skilled and able.**

11. I **have a strong dislike for** those who are cruel to animals.

arrest
capable
congratulate
despise
dispute
eventual
helm
humiliate
implore
insert
outrage
pierce
quiver
release
sullen

Circle the letter or letters of each correct answer. A question may have more than one correct answer.

1. Which of the following might be **congratulated?**
   (a) a winner
   (b) a bride and groom
   (c) a victim
   (d) an intruder

2. Which of the following could be **released?**
   (a) a statement to the press
   (b) a prisoner
   (c) a caged animal
   (d) a door catch

3. Which of the following happens **eventually?**
   (a) you are born
   (b) you die
   (c) a long winter comes to an end
   (d) practice makes perfect

4. Which of the following has a **helm?**
   (a) a racing car
   (b) a large truck
   (c) a ship
   (d) a fortress

5. Which of the following might be **humiliating?**
   (a) being routed in a contest
   (b) showing courage
   (c) being hailed as a hero
   (d) being jeered at

6. Which of the following would be an **outrage?**
   (a) jailing an innocent person
   (b) discovering a cure for a disease
   (c) banning free speech
   (d) consoling a person who is sad

7. Which of the following can be **pierced?**
   (a) the skin
   (b) the ears
   (c) the voice
   (d) fog

8. Which of the following would we want **arrested?**
   (a) a lawbreaker
   (b) the victim of a crime
   (c) the spread of a disease
   (d) a pessimist

20D ▷ Word Study

Each group of four words contains either two synonyms or two antonyms. Circle that pair. Then write S if they are synonyms or A if they are antonyms.

1. arrest	achieve	dispute	stop	_____
2. despise	cherish	extinguish	isolate	_____
3. valiant	crafty	temporary	fearless	_____
4. quarrel	feud	ramp	talon	_____
5. insert	astonish	confirm	astound	_____
6. sullen	amiable	capable	exquisite	_____
7. yield	waft	resist	prune	_____
8. banish	intend	welcome	persuade	_____
9. surround	raise	remember	recall	_____
10. relent	recall	lower	elevate	_____
11. detest	forsake	beg	implore	_____
12. fragile	forlorn	sad	capable	_____
13. create	recite	utilize	destroy	_____
14. capture	refine	release	console	_____
15. eliminate	remove	recommend	humiliate	_____

arrest

capable

congratulate

despise

dispute

eventual

helm

humiliate

implore

insert

outrage

pierce

quiver

release

sullen

Passage

Read the passage. Then answer the questions that follow it.

The Story of William Tell

In the town of Altdorf, Switzerland, stands a famous statue of William Tell, his son at his side, his crossbow slung over his shoulder. Although historians **dispute** William Tell's existence, and there is no evidence that he was a real person, Tell is a national hero to the Swiss people. He is a symbol of political and individual freedom.

Seven hundred years ago, the Swiss people were ruled by Austria. The governor of Switzerland was an Austrian named Gessler. Gessler **despised** the Swiss people. He did not consider them **capable** of ruling themselves. One day he decided to **humiliate** them. He put his cap on a pole and ordered everyone in the town of Altdorf who passed by to bow before it. The Swiss people regarded the cap as a symbol of Austrian rule, and they detested it. However, the people of Altdorf had no choice. **Sullenly,** they obeyed the order.

William Tell, a peasant from a nearby Swiss village, happened to be visiting Altdorf with his young son. Tell was famous for his skill as a boatman and was equally expert with the crossbow. He was also a proud man. The people of the village watched as he approached the cap. Would he bow his head before it? No one was surprised to see him walk past the cap with his head held high. The Austrian guards **arrested** him for his "crime" and took him before the governor.

Gessler had heard of William Tell's remarkable skill with the crossbow. It amused him to give his prisoner a choice: either go to prison or win freedom by shooting an apple from the top of his son's head at a hundred paces. Tell did not hesitate. After pacing out the distance, he removed two arrows from his **quiver.** He **inserted** the first one in the groove of his crossbow; the second arrow he tucked in his belt. He wound the spring of the crossbow and took careful aim. There was a tense silence. Those watching waited for him to **release** the arrow. When he did so, it flashed through the air, splitting the apple cleanly in two. The boy was unharmed. Gessler **congratulated** William Tell for demonstrating such skill. Then he asked what the second arrow was for.

William Tell looked him in the eye. He said, "If the first arrow had hurt my son, the second would have **pierced** your heart." Gessler was **outraged** by this reply. He ordered Tell locked up for the rest of his life. But the boat that was carrying him across the lake to prison ran into a storm. The frightened crew knew that William Tell was a skilled boatman. They untied him and **implored** him to take over. Tell seized the **helm.** While the crew cowered below, he steered the boat toward the rocky shore. At the last moment he leaped ashore and escaped.

Once free, he lay in wait at a place where he knew Gessler would pass. When the governor did so, the arrow from William Tell's bow found its mark. Gessler died instantly. The news of William Tell's deed spread quickly and made him a hero to the Swiss people. It helped to unite them in their struggle and **eventually** led to their freedom from Austrian rule.

▶ **Answer each of the following questions in the form of a sentence. If a question does not contain a vocabulary word from the lesson's word list, use one in your answer. Use each word only once.**

1. Do you think William Tell's **arrest** was unjust?

_____

_____

2. How did the people of Altdorf show their feelings when told to bow before the cap?

_____

_____

3. Why was it **humiliating** for the Swiss to bow before Gessler's cap?

_____

_____

4. What does it mean to say that historians **dispute** the existence of William Tell?

_____

_____

5. What were Gessler's feelings toward the Swiss people?

_____

_____

arrest
capable
congratulate
despise
dispute
eventual
helm
humiliate
implore
insert
outrage
pierce
quiver
release
sullen

6. Why did Gessler order William Tell to jail?

_____

_____

7. Why did Gessler think that Austria had a right to rule the Swiss people?

_____

_____

8. Why was everyone silent as they watched William Tell?

_____

_____

9. What did William Tell do with the two arrows?

_____

_____

10. What is the meaning of **quiver** as it is used in the passage?

_____

_____

11. What did William Tell intend to do with the second arrow?

_____

_____

12. How did Gessler react when the arrow split the apple in two?

_____

_____

13. Where was the crew while William Tell was at the **helm?**

_____

_____

14. How can we tell that the crew could not handle the boat?

_____

_____

15. Did Gessler's death have an immediate result?

_____

_____

FUN & FASCINATING FACTS

- To **humiliate** someone is to make that person look weak or foolish in the eyes of others. The word comes from the Latin *humilis,* which means "low." This Latin word in turn comes from an older Latin word, *humus,* which means "earth" or "dirt." To *humiliate* someone is to treat that person "like dirt." Incidentally, *humus* is the English word for the decayed vegetable matter that enriches soil.

  Humble (Word List 14) comes from the same Latin root. Someone of *humble* birth occupies a *low* position in society. To *humble* oneself is to *lower* oneself in the eyes of others.

  There is another noun formed from *humiliate,* in addition to *humiliation.* It is related in meaning, but with an important difference. *Humility* is the state of being humble. It is considered by many to be a desirable state, the opposite of being boastful or vain. *Humiliation* suggests being disgraced, having one's pride taken away.

- If you weep while **imploring** a person to do something, your pleading might have a better chance of succeeding. At least, that is what the word suggests. It comes from the Latin *plorare,* which means "to cry out" or "to weep."

- A **sullen** person is likely to shun the company of others or to be shunned by them. In either event, such a person is likely to be left alone. This should come as no surprise since the word comes from the Latin *solus,* which means "alone." For a number of other words formed from this Latin root see Lesson 13.

Crossword Puzzle Solve the crossword puzzle by studying the clues and filling in the answer boxes. Clues followed by a number are definitions of words in Lessons 17 through 20. The number gives the word list in which the answer to the clue appears.

Clues Across

1. To go with, to guide or protect (17)
4. To think well of (17)
9. Opposite of *higher*
11. To express pleasure for a person's success (20)
12. To lift up; to make higher (19)
13. Of great size; enormous (18)
14. A long, bitter quarrel (18)
16. To make a hole through (20)
17. A person who makes a living from the soil (18)
21. You write with this.
23. To take away the pride or self-respect of (20)
24. To fill with delight (19)
25. To warn someone that you might harm them (18)
26. Country in North Africa whose capital is Cairo

Clues Down

2. To end; to finish (17)
3. A custom handed down over time (19)
5. Used to make French fries
6. A person who is older (17)
7. To stop the movement or progress of (20)
8. A case for holding arrows (20)
10. Used to fight with
14. A building strong enough to be used for defense (18)
15. Something that gets in the way (18)
18. To send for (17)
19. An extra piece sewn or put in place (20)
20. To deserve (17)
21. Of little importance (18)
22. A tooth _____ or stomach _____

Pronunciation Key

Symbol	Key Words	Symbol	Key Words
a	cat	b	bed
ā	ape	d	dog
ä	cot, car	f	fall
â	bear	g	get
		h	help
e	ten, berry	j	jump
ē	me	k	kiss, call
		l	leg, bottle
i	fit	m	meat
ī	ice, fire	n	nose, kitten
		p	put
ō	go	r	red
ô	fall, for	s	see
oi	oil	t	top
ōo	look, pull	v	vat
ōō	tool, rule	w	wish
ou	out, crowd	y	yard
		z	zebra
u	up		
ʉ	fur, shirt	ch	chin, arch
		ŋ	ring, drink
ə	a in ago	sh	she, push
	e in agent	th	thin, truth
	i in pencil	*th*	then, father
	o in atom	zh	measure
	u in circus		
´	hospital (häs´ pit'l)		

A stress mark ´ is placed after a syllable that gets a primary stress, as in **vocabulary** (vō kab´ yə ler ē).